D1158144

Some other books by

JEAN LEE LATHAM

The Story of Eli Whitney
Man of the Monitor
Drake: The Man They Called a Pirate
Young Man in a Hurry
On Stage, Mr. Jefferson!
This Dear-Bought Land
Carry On, Mr. Bowditch
Trail Blazer of the Seas

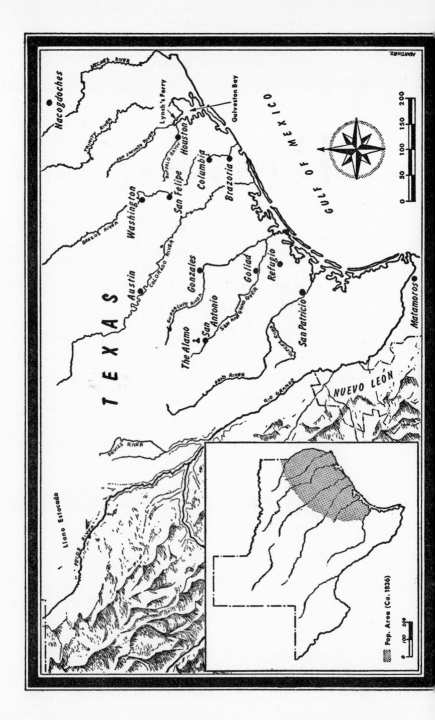

Retreat
to
Glory

THE STORY OF SAM HOUSTON

by
Jean Lee Latham

Harper & Row, Publishers • *New York, Evanston, and London*

To friends in Virginia, Tennessee, and Texas, who helped me so much with research.

J.L.L.

Contents

Contents

☆

Retreat
to
Glory

Black Sheep

Sam yawned, squirmed on the split-log bench, and wondered again what made afternoons in school so much longer than mornings. Especially on chilly, shut-in days. The log schoolhouse smelled of wood smoke, sweat, and damp wool.

How many more years would he have to spend shut up in school? If only he could live the way Father did, riding from one Army post to the other. Always on the move!

Time for geography. Sam yawned again, then stood with six others to recite the capitals of the states. He could have said them in his sleep. Why did school have to be so dull?

Just as the seven were saying "HART-ford, Con-NECT-i-cut, ON the—" the little ones in the front row started giggling.

Mr. Bennett rapped on his desk. "Silence!"

The little ones clapped their hands over their mouths, hunched their shoulders around their ears, and stared, big-eyed, at the teacher.

It must have been little Jimmy who started them giggling, Sam decided. Little Jimmy looked scared to death.

But Mr. Bennett did not look at the little ones. He said, "Sam Houston!"

"Yes, sir?"

"You will stay after school."

Oh, no! Not again! But Sam said, "Yes, sir."

At last school was over. Everybody but Sam shuffled through the door, then raced off with a whoop and a holler. He sat on the bench and waited. How long would it be today? Sometimes Mr. Bennett worked at his desk and let Sam sit there for an hour before he gave him "a good talking-to." Sam hoped he'd get around to the talking-to sooner today. He knew just how it would begin.

First Mr. Bennett would remind him that a boy of thirteen was Almost a Man. Mr. Bennett always talked in capitals when he was bawling you out. Then he'd talk about Sam's ancestors. He'd ask questions that Sam must answer:

"Who came to Virginia and carved Timber Ridge Plantation out of a wilderness? (My great-grandfather, sir.) Who built the stone church at Timber Ridge? (He did, sir.) Who gave the land and built this schoolhouse? (My father, sir.) Why do you think your father . . ."

After Mr. Bennett had covered the ancestors he would go on to Sam's brothers. It was bad enough having Honorable Ancestors. It was worse having Brothers

Who Behaved. Paxton, Robert, James, and John were older. Willie was younger.

"Why can't you Follow the Example of your older brothers?" Mr. Bennett would ask. "Why can't you Set an Example for Willie?"

So far Mr. Bennett had not talked about Sam's little sisters—Mary, Isabelle, and Eliza Ann.

"Someday," Sam said to himself, "I'll ask him about that. Should I Set an Example for them too?" But he knew he would not. He could get into enough trouble without talking back to grown-ups.

Mr. Bennett finally looked up. "Well, Sam?"

Sam got up slowly, thinking hard. What had he better say? "Yes, sir?"

"What were you doing *this* time?"

"When, sir?"

"Why did the little ones start giggling?"

"When we were reciting the capitals of the states, sir?"

"You know when! What were you doing?"

"I'm not sure, sir, but maybe I was wiggling my ears."

"*What!*"

"You know how it is, sir. When we recite the capitals the words sort of—march. Maybe I was keeping time. Like this, sir." He kept time with his ears as he recited, "AU-gus-ta, MA-aine, ON the—"

"Stop it!"

"Yes, sir. I'm sorry, sir. But you asked me—"

"That's enough! Sam Houston . . ."

After Mr. Bennett had covered the ancestors and the brothers he shook his head. "I simply can't understand you. You're the brightest boy in this school. You've read more books than any ten others. But what is ever going to become of you?"

"I'll be a soldier, sir! Like my father! Someday I'll be the next Major Sam Houston of Timber Ridge Plantation!"

"Heaven help Timber Ridge if—" Mr. Bennett stopped.

"Sir?"

Mr. Bennett turned red. "Nothing. That is all. You may go."

"Yes, sir. Thank you, sir!" Sam saluted, wheeled, and marched out the door. He stood a moment looking about at Timber Ridge—the big house with its tall white pillars, the barns and slave cabins, the fields, the pastures and the woods.

What had Mr. Bennett meant when he said "Heaven help Timber Ridge"? Just because Sam said he was going to be a soldier like Father? Of course Father was gone a lot of the time on his tours of inspection. And every so often he sold some land. And he had sold most of their slaves to Uncle Matthew. But why did Mr. Bennett say "Heaven help Timber Ridge"?

A shrill voice interrupted his thoughts. He followed

the noise around the stone church. It sounded like—yes, it was—little Jimmy's sister Genevieve, teacher's-pet-tattletale Genevieve, scolding Jimmy.

"If a gentleman ever struck a woman," Sam said to himself, "I'd smack her good!"

"Go on, Fraidy Cat!" Genevieve ordered. "Tell him!"

Sam grinned down at Jimmy. "Tell me what?"

"It was my fault," Jimmy muttered. "I d-d-drew a picture on my slate."

"That so? Must have been a good one. Let's see it."

"I r-r-rubbed it out. I'm sorry I let you take the blame, Sam." He burrowed his head against Sam and began to sob. "B-b-b-b-but I was scared!"

"That's all right," Sam told him. "It's all over now."

"That doesn't make it all right!" Genevieve said sharply. "He let *you* be punished for what *he* did! He's got to make it up to you!"

That Genevieve! Sam counted to ten and then said, "Of course he's going to make it up to me. Tell you what you do, Jimmy. You wait till you're as big as I am and there are other little ones in school, and someday you take the blame for one of them."

"That's all?"

"That's all."

"Gee!" Jimmy swiped at his tears. "Thanks!"

Genevieve sniffed. "That does *not* make it up to you. You were punished for what you didn't do. That's not right!"

Sam grinned. "But think of all the times I don't get punished for something I did do. I'm still ahead."

She stamped her foot. "But it's not right! You had to tell a lie to take the blame. That's a sin!"

"No, I didn't tell a lie," Sam declared. "I just said *maybe*. I said *maybe* I wiggled my ears. Like this."

He wiggled them and Jimmy giggled. "So that's all, Jimmy. Just remember—when you're as big as I am—"

"Yes, sir, Sam! Someday I'll be a Black Sheep, too! Maybe," he added cheerfully, "I'll be the Black Sheep of the whole state of Virginia!" And Jimmy raced off.

"No!" Sam yelled. "Jimmy!"

But Jimmy was gone.

"Now look what you've done!" Genevieve said.

"But I didn't mean—"

"No wonder people say 'Poor Mrs. Houston! With a son like Sam!'" Genevieve strutted off, looking pleased with herself.

Sam watched her go. *His poor mother.* Did people really say that? Or did Genevieve just make it up? He didn't make that much trouble . . . did he?

Suddenly he snapped his fingers and hurried toward the house. There was something he had forgotten to do last Saturday night. Sunday had been March 2, his birthday. The night before he always checked over his New Year's Resolutions. If he had broken any, he wrote them again.

Black Sheep

He went into the library and took his favorite book from the shelf—*Manual of Arms.* Father had drilled soldiers by those rules in the Revolutionary War. Sam had learned to read out of it. He could read "Halt!" "Forward march!" and "Shoulder arms!" before he started to school.

He took his resolutions from the book, stretched on the floor in front of the fire, and began to read.

1. I will not be the Black Sheep any more.
2. When Father is away I will be more help to Mother.
3. I will not yell at my older brothers even if they all start bossing me at the same time.

Sam read on. He shook his head and began to write. He copied the whole list. He drew a line under Number 3, about not yelling at his older brothers. That was the hardest one to keep. He got along pretty well when Father was home. But tomorrow Father would ride away on another tour of the Army posts.

"Tomorrow," Sam told himself, "you get up at the crack of dawn!" That was the morning—the only morning—that Sam never overslept. He was always down at the end of the lane, waiting to salute as Father rode away. Silly. He had started doing it when he was just a little fellow. Now it was a sort of joke between him and Father. So, tomorrow morning . . .

The next morning the *clop-clop* of hoofbeats wakened Sam. Oh, no! How could he have overslept? He scrambled out of bed and raced the length of the wide hall to the front of the house. Maybe it wasn't Father's horse. He looked down on the tree-lined lane that led to the road. He was just in time to see Father, in his major's uniform, reach the end of the lane.

As Sam watched, Father stopped and raised his hand in salute. He looked in both directions. Then slowly he lowered his hand and rode on.

Sam ran back to his room. If he rode across the fields he could get ahead of Father. There'd be fences to jump. . . . Big Red could jump them. . . .

Sam remembered the day the huge stallion had thrown one of the men and tried to trample him to death. Since then no one had ridden Red—no one but Sam. And nobody knew that he had done it.

He scrambled into his clothes and started tiptoeing down the stairs. The family were still at breakfast.

He heard Paxton say, "Where's Sam?"

Robert, the second oldest, laughed. "Out by the road, playing soldier. That's *one* thing we can always depend on Sam to do."

"Boys, please!" Mother had the most beautiful voice Sam had ever heard—low and warm, with a sort of smile running through it.

Paxton was impatient. "Mother, you know we're only

8

trying to help you. When Father's away, someone has to keep Sam in line."

Sam opened the door, slid out, closed it softly, and darted around the house to the barn. Thank goodness Old Adam wasn't puttering around.

Big Red laid back his ears and rolled his eyes when Sam put the saddle on him.

"None of your tricks, Red!" Sam always tried to sound sure of himself when he talked to Red. He took a deep breath, then squatted near the wicked hoofs to tighten the cinch.

He was out of the barn and mounted before anyone saw him. Red was pawing the air.

"No, Marse Sam! No!" Old Adam shouted and came hobbling toward them.

"Get out of the way!" Sam yelled.

But Adam just stood there, right in the path, his eyes staring out of his black face.

Sam wheeled Red toward a hedge. It was close—too close. But the big stallion leaped, clearing it by a foot.

"You magnificent brute!" Sam whispered. He gave the big horse his head, letting him race through the fields, leaping one creek twice. That was what it took to ride him! Just stick till he settled down.

Sam urged Red toward the second jump. Three more fences and he'd be waiting at the bend when Father got there.

But Sam was a little later reaching the place than he had thought he would be. Father came around the bend just in time to see Red clear the fence.

"Sam!" Father had never sounded so stern. He pulled Dusty to a halt and sat there, staring.

Evidently the wild ride had satisfied Red. He stood like a statue. Sam grinned and saluted.

Father did not return the salute. He did not smile.

Heartsick, Sam lowered his hand. "But, sir, nobody ever *said* I couldn't ride him."

No answer.

"It's not the first time, Father. Red's wonderful. I just let him work off a little steam, and then he settles down."

"So you've ridden him before?" Still that stern, cold voice.

"Yes, sir."

"How many people know you've ridden him?"

"Nobody, sir."

"Why not?"

"All right! I guess I knew I shouldn't ride him! And I sneaked him out when nobody was around to see me. But, sir, we get along just fine. Red and I—we're kind of alike."

"So?"

"Yes, sir. Red and I—we've both got to work off steam. Then we settle down . . . for a while. I think maybe Red settles down better than I do. I wish he could be my horse!"

"You brought him across the fields?"

"Yes, sir."

"And jumped fences?"

"Yes, sir."

"What if he had broken a leg?"

"But he wouldn't, sir. He's a wonderful jumper. Even —" He had better not talk about the first jump.

"You will take him home by the road. No more jumps."

"Yes, sir. No, sir."

"You will not ride him again."

"But, sir . . . No, sir. Never again. But, sir, it's important for a soldier to be a good horseman, isn't it?"

"You think you'd make a good soldier?"

"Yes, sir! I'm strong! I can run faster and jump higher and swim farther than any boy anywhere near my size. And I haven't been licked in a fight since I was ten. Not even by a boy that weighed twenty pounds more than I did."

"And you've had lots of fights?"

"Yes, sir! Dozens. Once I had two fights in—" Something in Father's eyes stopped him. "Isn't it important for a soldier to be a good fighter?"

"Yes." Father was grim. "You'd probably make a pretty good volunteer. I remember how it was in the war. General Washington had plenty of those. They'd join up for a skirmish. Then they'd fade like snow in July. A real soldier has to do more than fight."

"What, sir?"

"He has to be ready. He has to stay ready. Sometimes he has to wait and wait for orders. Then he obeys orders—whether he understands the reason for them or not. *A soldier obeys!* Subordination! That is the must-be of an army! Subordination. Never heard that word before, I suppose? Unquestioning obedience to authority!"

"Oh. . . ." After a silence Sam asked, "Father?"

"Yes?"

"What if—the next time you come home—I don't have a single black mark on my record?"

"I'd fall down in a dead faint." Suddenly Father smiled. "And I'd offer to take you with me on my next inspection tour."

"Thank you! It'll be the very next time, sir!"

"Good. Sam, I'm sorry I was harsh. You see—"

But Red had stood still long enough. He bolted and didn't stop until he turned into the lane at Timber Ridge.

Old Adam came running, wringing his hands. "Man alive, I thought you'd be dead!"

"Red's all right, soon as he works off steam." Sam dismounted and walked toward the barn. "I'm sorry I yelled at you, Adam."

Adam grinned. "That's all right, Marse Sam. I don't

pay no never-mind to your conniptions. Like heat light-
nin'. Big flash, but don't kill nobody."

"No more conniptions, Adam." Sam grinned. "Bet
you don't believe me. Just wait and see!"

Paxton, Robert, James, and John hurried up, all
shouting at the same time. Sam clenched his teeth and
said nothing.

"Red's all right!" Adam said. "Not a scratch!"

"He'd better be all right!" Then Robert yelled at
Sam. "What did you mean, taking him out, risking an
accident, just before Mr. Martin came for him? When
he's already been sold and Father has the money?"

"No! No! Father couldn't sell Red! Why? *Why?*"

"Because," Robert said abruptly, "he needed the
money."

"When—when's Mr. Martin coming?"

"This morning."

Sam dashed around the barn and raced toward the
woods. He couldn't stand to see someone take Red away.

He forgot about school till the sun was twelve o'clock
high. Then it was no use to go. That evening he had a
row with Paxton. The next day . . .

When Father came home he said, "Well, Sam?"

"The next time, sir!" Sam promised. "The very next
time!"

A year later he was still saying "The next time, sir!"

The fall of 1807, when Sam was fourteen, Father died
suddenly.

The Runaway

Numb with sorrow, Sam listened to the minister's words:

"Major Sam Houston did not die in battle. But he did die a hero in the service of his country. He left a proud name to his sons."

Sam's throat ached. *He* was the one with Father's name, and he had not lived up to it.

The week after the funeral a shocked Uncle Matthew was talking with Mother. "I can't believe it, Elizabeth. Up to his ears in debt! How could it happen? A man who was once worth—"

"When God measures the worth of a man," Mother asked, "what do you think he measures? His money bags or his heart?"

"I know, I know! A fine man. But to think he didn't leave a thing!"

Mother lifted her chin. "He left a proud name to his sons."

"It would be hard to rear nine children on just 'a

proud name.' Of course our home will always be your home, and—"

"No, Matthew. We have the land in Tennessee."

"Four hundred acres of wilderness! Elizabeth, you can't face that kind of life!"

"Why not? My ancestors were pioneers, too, Matthew. I hope I have as much spunk as my grandmother had."

"But she had a husband to help her! To clear the land, to build the home, to—"

"I have men to help me. My sons."

Uncle Matthew said nothing. He looked from one boy to the other. Sam had a feeling that Uncle Matthew looked longest at him.

"I'll show him!" Sam told himself. "I'll show the whole world! Nobody will ever call me 'Black Sheep' again!"

The day came when they said good-by to the tall white pillars of Timber Ridge. Two wagons held all they had left of that life.

Uncle Matthew was there, still pleading with Mother not to go. "Elizabeth, have you the faintest idea what the road is like between here and Knoxville, Tennessee?"

"Not the faintest!" The smile was running through Mother's voice again.

"Well, I've been over that road, and—"

"Please, Matthew! Don't say anything to scare a 'lone widow-woman with nine children.' "

Uncle Matthew did not smile. His face was grim. Then he shook his head and sighed. "It's no use, is it? God bless you—and God help you."

After six days on the road Sam understood why Uncle Matthew had looked so grim. Each day the road was worse. More mudholes where the wagons bogged down until the horses could not move them. There was nothing to do but unload, get the wagons out, and load again.

More rivers to ford. Banks so steep that they tied ropes on the back axles and snubbed them around trees to hold back the wagons as the horses stumbled and slid down the steep banks.

By the fourth day Sam felt as though every joint in his body needed grease. Sometimes he was so tired he fell asleep over his supper. Sometimes he was so tired that he lay and ached instead of sleeping.

But day after day he said "Yes, sir!" to Robert. Paxton was sick. He had a bad cough that he couldn't seem to throw off. So Robert was boss—and a very bossy boss. Sometimes Sam walked ahead, scouting for game. Sometimes he worked off his temper splitting wood for the fire.

At last one evening Robert slapped him on the shoulder. "Sam, you're all right. You know, Mother, I think we left our Black Sheep back in Virginia."

Sam was the first one to laugh. "Yes, sir, we certainly did!" Then everybody laughed but Willie. He scowled.

"Sam's the best brother a boy ever had!"

Mother smiled. "Don't let your lip freeze that way, Willie. A buzzard might roost on it."

And Willie had to smile too.

Nineteen days . . . twenty . . . twenty-one. Sam felt like an old plow horse, plodding his last furrow. Then the road widened to a cluster of log cabins. Knoxville!

Eliza Ann, who was the youngest—only eight—looked about. Her chin trembled. "Aren't there any *really* houses anywhere?"

But Sam grinned. Knoxville! Almost there! Maybe the road from here on wouldn't be so bad.

A man said, "Better give your horses a rest. Road to Maryville ain't much."

It took three days to travel less than twenty miles.

Maryville—just a smaller cluster of log cabins on a road that was nothing but a muddy trail.

In Maryville a man said, "So you're heading for Baker's Creek? Better give your horses a rest. From here on—well, there ain't any road to speak of."

It took almost three days to go the last ten miles to a branch of Baker's Creek.

"Four hundred acres of wilderness." That was what Uncle Matthew had called it.

Sam drew a deep breath. It had been worth it! Wooded hills all around. Beyond, the blue haze of mountains.

"Not much now," Robert said, "but when we've improved it . . ."

They cleared land. They squared logs. They built a home. Just two log cabins with a roofed-over space between them. The settlers called that roofed-over space a "dog-trot."

More land to clear for a garden. More land for cornfields. Sam watched the clearing creep into the forest. Ugly stump-strewn fields. Was this "improving" the land?

He worked off his temper splitting firewood.

"Time to plow!" Robert said. "We've got to get the crops in."

Then the long dull days began. Get up. Plow. Go to bed. Get up. Plow. Go to bed. Then the planting. Get up. Plant. Go to bed.

One morning Sam sneaked off before anyone else was awake and went fishing. He came back with quite a string. Another time he went hunting. He came back empty-handed.

One evening he came back to find all four older brothers talking with Mother.

"Come on in, Sam," Robert called. "We've been waiting for you."

"I won't be a farmer!" Sam yelled. "I won't! I hate it!"

"Why don't you wait till you hear what I have to say before you start raving?" Robert suggested. "We've decided you're not worth your salt as a farmer. We've got another job for you."

"Sorry I blew up."

"You're going to work in Mr. Weber's store in Maryville. Think we can depend on you for that?"

"Yes, sir! Anything's better than farming!"

But when Sam entered the store he shivered. How dim and crowded! Worse than the schoolhouse in bad weather!

And the long dull days began. Get up. Sweep out. Weigh sugar. Weigh salt. Weigh nails. Measure calico. Yes, ma'am. No, ma'am. Yes, sir. No, sir. Close the store. Go to bed.

Sam was alone one day when a tall, straight Indian boy—he looked about Sam's age—came in, walking with his silent, toed-in tread. He laid a bundle of pelts on the counter. Sam wished he could talk Indian. He smiled at the boy.

To his surprise the Indian said, "I wish to trade for a kettle. And a hatchet."

"Yes, sir." Sam held out his hand. "I'm Sam Houston."

For a moment the boy hesitated, then he shook hands. "I am called Blue Feather."

"Did you catch all these animals yourself? I mean—trap or shoot or whatever you do?"

Blue Feather gave him a long, level stare. "Yes. I did not steal them."

Sam's ears burned. "Please, I didn't mean that. I was just thinking what it would be like to live where you could hunt instead of—like this."

Blue Feather looked around the crowded store. "I could not live this way. It would be like prison."

"Where do you live?"

Blue Feather motioned southeast. "On Hiwassee Island. In the village of Oo-loo-te-ka. He is a chief of the Cherokees."

"Is it far?"

"No, not far. Two sleeps."

Blue Feather took his kettle and his hatchet. He turned toward the door.

"Good luck!" Sam called.

Blue Feather paused. He looked back. "The Great Spirit pity you." He went out into the sunlight and fresh air. The store seemed darker after he had gone.

The days dragged by. Get up . . . sweep out . . .

One night Sam filled a sack with food. He made a list of what he had taken. He wrote:

> Dear Mr. Weber
>   I am taking this food instead of wages. If I owe
> you anything I will pay it when I come to trade.
>   Sam Houston

The Runaway

He left a note to be delivered to his mother:

Dear Mother
    I can't stand this shut-in life. I have gone to
live with the Indians. I hope you will miss me, but
not too much.

                                    Your loving son
                                        Sam

He made a bundle of his books and clothes. The books
took up more room. A Bible and some poetry—Robert
Burns, and Pope's translation of the *Iliad*. He liked
words with a swing to them. He hefted the sack of food.
Did he have enough? Blue Feather had said Hiwassee
Island was only two sleeps from Maryville. That meant
two nights—just two days' travel. Yes, this was enough.

The afternoon of the fourth day Sam looked across a
river toward a hilly island. Two Indian boys were fishing
in a dugout canoe. Sam hailed them. Was that Hiwassee
Island? It was. He flopped down on the riverbank and
grinned. Finally! He had never been so hungry in his
life!

Soon he was in Oo-loo-te-ka's village. Odd. He had
not known that the Cherokees lived in log cabins. Better-
made cabins than the ones in Maryville, too.

They must use their cabins for nothing but sleeping.
All work seemed to be going on out-of-doors. That
made sense! He watched a girl pour grains of browned
corn into a hollowed-out tree stump. She began pounding it into a coarse meal.

A voice said, "Sam Houston is welcome." It was Blue Feather.

Sam started to say, "What was that joke about only two sleeps?"

"You would like to see Oo-loo-te-ka?" Blue Feather asked. "I will take you to his wigwam."

Another odd thing. They lived in log cabins, but they called them wigwams. He must remember all these things. Sam followed Blue Feather.

Oo-loo-te-ka was tall, straight, and dignified enough for a king.

Blue Feather said, "It is Sam Houston. From the trader's wigwam in Maryville. Our brother has honored us. He has traveled two sleeps to visit our village."

Two sleeps! He hadn't been halfway to Hiwassee in two sleeps! The last two days he had run till his tongue hung out!

Oo-loo-te-ka said, "Our brother is welcome. My wigwam is yours. You will eat with us."

It was all Sam could do to keep from wolfing his food.

After they had eaten, the chief said, "Our brother brings a message?"

"I—I—" The words stuck in his throat. What nerve to come barging in and say "I want to live with you." Sam gulped. "I wish to serve you. I wish to be one of your braves."

Something flickered in Oo-loo-te-ka's eyes. Was he laughing?

22

The Runaway

Sam stumbled on. "I—I am the son of a soldier. I think I'll make a good fighter."

"We live at peace. Oo-loo-te-ka means 'He Puts the Drum Away.' "

"Oh. . . . Then I can be a hunter."

The chief shook his head. "A gun makes too much noise. Will our brother stand up?" He measured Sam with a glance. "Our brother's legs are long. Perhaps he can run?"

"Yes, sir!"

"Perhaps our brother can be trained for a messenger. How far can he run in a day?"

"In a day? I never tried to run a whole day!"

"Tomorrow we shall see."

It was still dark when a hand on his shoulder wakened Sam. He jumped and sat up.

"What is it?"

Blue Feather said, "Shhh! Our brother starts like a frightened deer. Come."

Sam followed him from the cabin. "What did you expect me to do? Wakened out of a sound sleep. Of course I jumped!"

"A warrior can never be startled. He never moves until he knows who is beside him—friend or foe."

"Oh. . . ." So he had told Oo-loo-te-ka that he'd make a good warrior? He seemed to have a few things to learn!

Blue Feather said, "It is time to go."

"Don't we have breakfast first?"

"We carry our food." Blue Feather gave Sam a small pouch of pounded corn.

If that was all the food they were taking, they'd not go very far.

Across the river Blue Feather set off at an easy jog up a trail. Sam followed.

Blue Feather turned. "Shhhh. Our brother makes more noise than six frightened deer."

Sam tried to run more quietly. He watched the ground to keep from stepping on twigs. The trail was narrow. Branches lashed across his face and stung his eyes. Finally he was panting and falling behind.

Blue Feather stopped and waited for Sam. His voice was kind. "Our brother must not be sad. He is weak, but it is not his fault. Rest here awhile, then follow me." He ran on.

Weak! No one had ever called him that! Sam had a notion to dash after Blue Feather and . . . But he had another notion not to. He knelt by a brook and sloshed water on his sweating face. He drank thirstily. He'd do as Blue Feather said—rest awhile and then follow.

He was hungry. That was what was the matter with him. He was starving! He ate the parched corn. He drank more water. He stretched out on the ground. He'd rest a little while.

When he wakened the sun was four o'clock high.

The Runaway

Where was Blue Feather? Ten minutes later Sam jumped when Blue Feather spoke. He had not heard a sound.

"How far did you go?" Sam asked.

"Halfway."

"What do you mean—'halfway'?"

"Half of one sleep. When we are in the village again, it will be twenty-five miles. That is one sleep."

Sam wanted to yell "You're crazy! It's a lie!" But that wouldn't be any way to keep a friend on Hiwassee.

When they got back to the village the boys gathered around them. How far had their brother run?

"He is very weak," Blue Feather said. "But it is not his fault. He has not been trained as we are."

Sam's face burned. There it was again. *Weak!* But compared to Blue Feather, he was a poor excuse. He couldn't measure up. Soon Oo-loo-te-ka would tell him to go back where he belonged.

"Perhaps our brother will have skill with the bow and arrow," Blue Feather said.

The next morning they took Blue Feather's bow and a quiver of arrows. A crowd of boys followed them.

Blue Feather's bow seemed to be very easy to handle. Quick as a flash he planted five arrows in a distant sapling, one under the other, in a straight line. He handed the bow and an arrow to Sam.

Sam fitted the arrow and started to pull back on the string. How stiff the bow was! He set his teeth and jerked. The arrow slipped from his fingers. It did not go halfway to the tree. The next time he pulled steadily, but not one of his five arrows even hit the tree.

Blue Feather's voice was kind. "It is not our brother's fault. He has not been trained."

Again Sam's face burned. Wasn't there any way he could measure up?

"Perhaps our brother can swim?" Blue Feather asked.

Sam smiled. That was certainly one thing he could do! He could swim like a fish!

They went to the river. The crowd of boys followed.

"How far can our brother swim under water?" Blue Feather asked.

"Under water? Holding my breath? I don't know. I never tried it very long. What's the sense of it?"

Blue Feather was patient. "If our brother wishes to reach a deer without being seen, how else can he get close to it?" He stripped and slid into the water. He floated on his back and waited for Sam.

Sam stripped, took a deep breath, and dived. With the speed he had, he'd really show them something! He'd cross the river and come up on the other side. He'd win this time, or he'd . . .

At last he had to come up, gasping for air. No sign of Blue Feather. It seemed forever before his black head emerged. He rolled over and swam toward Sam. He wasn't even breathing hard.

Sam knew he had failed again.

The Raven

Just at dawn one morning the next spring Sam left the village with Blue Feather and his brother The Singer. Sam had a quiver of arrows over his left shoulder, a bundle of deerskin over the other, a bow in his right hand, and a pouch of dried corn hanging from his belt.

Just wait till they saw him in Maryville! Maybe they wouldn't even know him. He had grown about four inches. He was bare to the waist and almost as brown as an Indian. He wore deerskin trousers and moccasins.

The Singer began to chant. His voice was solemn but his eyes danced.

> Our brother The Raven is a mighty hunter.
> The Mother Deer warns her little ones:
> Beware of The Raven!
> Even the mighty stag with twenty antlers
> Flees at the sound of his name!
> The Raven!

A warm glow started in Sam's chest and spread through his body. That was his name now. Co-lon-neh

—The Raven. Oo-loo-te-ka had given him the name. Oo-loo-te-ka had said, "This is my son The Raven."

At the river they launched a canoe. With a flourish The Singer motioned for Sam to get in the prow. He knelt there facing them. They shoved off. The Singer began another chant, keeping time to the paddles:

> Our brother goes to the Land of the White Man.
> For five sleeps there will be a vacant place by
> our campfire!

He rolled his eyes to the heavens and howled like a lonely wolf:

> Oooooow! A cloud hangs over our village!
> Ooooow! Our hearts will be heavy for five sleeps!
> Oooooow!

Sam laughed out loud and The Singer laughed with him. They crossed the river. Sam jumped out and raised his hand in salute.

"The Raven returns in five sleeps!" He set off at a jog for Maryville.

He could have entered the village the second night, but he waited until morning. Then, when he knew the village would be astir, he strode, Indian-straight, down the road and into the store.

Mr. Weber glanced at him, blinked, then stared. "Sam Houston!"

The Raven

"My name is Co-lon-neh. That means The Raven."

" 'The Raven,' eh? Sounds like it might be Indian talk for 'Black Sheep.' Fits you, all right."

"The Raven is a good-luck bird of the Cherokees. It is an honored name." Sam put the bundle of deerskins on the counter and handed Mr. Weber a list. "The Raven has come to trade. He wants these things for his deerskins. He goes now to the home of his mother. He will return in one sleep."

He marched from the store and through the village, leaving a buzz of whispers behind him. He set out at a jog toward home.

Mother and the girls were alone. Mother was first to recognize him. "Sam! Sam, dear!" She kissed him. "How you've grown!" Then she asked, "Where *are* your clothes?"

He laughed. "You answered that yourself, Mother. I left them four inches behind me."

She did not ask "How could you run away?" She did not say "I hope you have come to your senses." She only said, "You look happy, Sam. Tell me about it."

"I *am* happy. Because I've had such a rough time of it. You know what they said of me at first, Mother? 'Our brother is weak, but it is not his fault.' "

"Weak? You!"

He told of the endurance that he had had to learn. "They're wonderful people. We call Indians 'savages.'

Not the Cherokees. They live at peace. They honor the old people. They are kind to their children. And they are so full of fun!"

"Really?" Mother looked surprised. "They always seem so stern and so—so shut-face."

"That's only around strangers. At home they are always joking." He told of The Singer's chants.

Sam could feel a question in the air: "What's going to become of you?"

"I'm stronger and better trained than any white man I know," he said. "And I'm not letting my brains go to seed. I'm reading as much as I did back in Virginia. I don't have so many books, but . . . " He linked his hands around one knee and began to recite from the *Iliad*. He was still reciting when the boys got home.

Robert said, "So you've come to your senses, have you?"

"Hold your temper!" Sam told himself. But in ten minutes he and Robert were shouting at each other.

That night after the others were asleep, Sam and his mother talked late.

"It's no use, Mother. You see that, don't you?" he pleaded. "I wouldn't be any help to you if I stayed. I'd just make trouble. You *can* see it, can't you?"

"Sam, dear . . . " After a long silence she said, "We'd better get some sleep. I'll fix you a good breakfast in the morning."

"No breakfast, Mother. The Raven travels on an empty stomach."

"Then I'll pack you enough food for—"

"The Raven has food." He showed her the pouch of dried corn. "If The Raven needs more, he'll get it with an arrow."

Then next morning he was at the store when it opened.

Mr. Weber shook his head. "Your deerskins won't pay for all these things, Sam. You'll still owe thirty dollars."

Thirty dollars! Sam looked at the stack of presents. He could not take presents to one and forget another. "Then I'll sign an IOU."

Mr. Weber hesitated, then shrugged. "I guess it's all right. Your brothers own a share in the store now. They're really making something of themselves. Yes, sir. I guess they'll be good for your debts if you're not."

"The Raven will pay his own debts! He'll bring more pelts when he comes to trade again!"

Mr. Weber shrugged and handed Sam a slip of paper.

Sam wrote: "IOU $30.00. Sam Houston." He made a bundle of his presents and left the store.

Thirty dollars in debt! The words dogged his footsteps. But back at Hiwassee with his presents he forgot the debt.

The next time he came to Maryville he had a bigger bundle of pelts—and a longer list. He signed another

IOU. The next time . . . and the time after that . . .

The spring of 1812, just before he was nineteen, Sam came again. Blue Feather and The Singer were with him. It took all three of them to carry Sam's pelts. Sam towered over the other two. He had long since topped six feet, and he was still growing.

"Greetings!" he said. "The Raven comes to—"

Mr. Weber cut him short. "No. No more credit. Not till you pay up what you owe. One hundred dollars."

"What!"

"You heard me. If you don't believe it, add the figures yourself."

Boze Hollis, about Sam's age and two hundred pounds of bully, got up off a box and laughed. "Haw, haw! So the mighty Raven has come a cropper, has he?"

Sam stared blindly at his IOU's. At last he said, "The Raven will trade for these skins. Or he will send them back to Hiwassee. He will stay in Maryville until he has paid his debt."

Mr. Weber rubbed his chin. "Well, I guess it's all right. Your brothers will be good for it if—"

"The Raven will pay his own debt!"

"You're going to have quite a little stay in Maryville!" Mr. Weber said. He haggled over the trading.

Sam made two bundles of the presents. He gave them to Blue Feather and The Singer. He walked from the store with them.

"Tell my father that The Raven must stay here for a

while. He must pay a debt. Then he will return to Hi-wassee."

"It will be many sleeps?" The Singer asked.

One hundred dollars! How could he ever pay it? "It will be many moons."

For once The Singer had no chant. "Our hearts will be with our brother."

Sam watched them walk away. He turned and started toward his home. As he passed people on the road through Maryville, he heard a buzz of whispers. This time the whispers were different. He heard snickers, too. Everybody knew about his debt. People were laughing at him! He set his teeth.

Boze Hollis swaggered into the road and blocked Sam's path. "Well, Mr. Indian, what you think you'll—"

"Get . . . out . . . of . . . my . . . way."

"Why don't you *make* me?"

Sam's hands moved so fast they were a blur. Boze landed with a thud in the road. Sam walked on.

Behind him he heard laughter. Someone yelled, "Hey, Boze, did you tell him to *make* you?"

Sam did not turn. He walked on, smiling. But the smile was gone when he reached home.

Thank goodness, Mother was alone. Her voice was loving. "Sam, dear!" Then she smiled. "I declare, you're still growing."

"You know about it, don't you?" he said. "One hundred dollars in debt."

"What for, Sam? Presents for your friends?"

"How'd you guess?"

"You're like your father." The smile was running through her voice. "I could never do a thing with him! Every so often he'd declare he was going to change his ways. But the next time he came home he'd bring presents for everybody. I remember once he brought me the most beautiful piece of silk for a dress. For once I almost scolded him. I said, 'Dear, I don't *need* a dress!' You know what he said, Sam? 'But I needed to get it for you.'"

"What did you say to that?"

"Nothing, Sam. I just kissed him. . . . He was a wonderful man. Do you remember what the minister said?"

"Yes, Mother." He had to stop a moment to steady his voice. "'He left a proud name to his sons.' I remember how I felt when I heard that. How I swore I'd live up to that name."

"You're making a good start." Mother's eyes were twinkling.

"What!"

"No other son of your father is one hundred dollars in debt for presents."

"Mother!" He laughed and hugged her. After a moment he said, "I'm not going to give you any trouble, Mother. No rowing with my brothers this time. That's a promise. I'll keep my tongue between my teeth."

The Raven

"It's good to have you home. The family seems sort of small."

"I know." He couldn't think of anything else to say. Paxton had died, and little Isabelle. He had not been there for either funeral. It would have been too late before word could reach him.

"Well! The girls and I had better get busy making you some clothes. And I'll have the cobbler do you a pair of shoes. We have some credit there in leather. He'll be glad to work it off."

A feeling of shame crawled through Sam. "I've heard of beggars with 'nothing but the clothes on their backs.' I'm worse than that."

"Dear Sam!" was all she said.

The next week, dressed in new homespun trousers and coat, Sam rode into Maryville with Willie. There was to be a program at Porter's Academy—music, orations, and a spelling bee. Willie was a student there. Doing fine, everybody said. All the brothers were doing fine— all but Sam.

"I'd rather take a beating than go to this," Sam thought. But he could not disappoint Willie. Outside the door of the hall he took a deep breath, got ready to smile, and followed Willie inside. The buzz of whispers began. Necks craned. Eyes stared.

Boze Hollis was there. He got up and took his time looking Sam over. "How about it, Willie? Going to civilize him?"

Willie flushed and started to speak, but Sam gripped his arm.

"Easy!" he whispered. He said, "Willie's going to *try* to civilize me. Think it'll work?"

The whispers stopped. A chuckle ran over the crowd.

Boze scowled and tried again. "How d'you feel in white man's clothes, Mr. Indian?"

"Awful. Especially the shoes. They're stiff."

Another chuckle from the crowd.

Boze spoke louder. "Think you'll understand white man's talk?"

Sam could feel the blood beating in his ears. But he was still smiling. "If I hear any words I don't know, Boze, I'll ask you—to spell them!"

Laughter rocked the crowd this time. Everybody knew that Boze hadn't finished the third reader. Boze sat down muttering.

The last thing on the program was the spelling bee. Willie was one of the captains to choose up sides.

"I want my brother Sam," he said. "Is that all right?"

The crowd was good-natured about it. "Sure! Go ahead!"

Boze said, "Too bad to waste your first choice, Willie. You could have had a *good* speller."

When the match ended, Sam had won.

Everybody clapped. Someone yelled, "Sam, you ought to be a teacher!"

Boze haw-hawed.

Sam spoke before he thought. "That's what I'm going to do. Open a school!"

Silence. The buzz of whispers again.

Boze got up. "Good idea, Mr. Indian. You ought to get three or four pupils—if you're cheap enough. *Real* teachers charge six dollars. What'll *you* charge? Deerskins?"

"I'll charge eight dollars!" Sam yelled. What in the name of sense had made him say that? He couldn't back down. He went on just as loudly. "One third in cash, one third in corn, delivered to the mill, and one third in calico! School will begin as soon as spring planting is done!" He strode out, flung himself on his horse, and rode off alone.

He shouldn't have walked out on Willie. But he couldn't go back. When he got home, everybody had gone to bed. He waited up for Willie.

Willie came in, beaming. "Sam, that's great! You'll make a wonderful teacher!"

"Why?"

"Remember back at Timber Ridge? How every time something happened the teacher blamed you?"

"Most of the time he was right. Does *that* make a good teacher?"

"No, Sam. But sometimes something wasn't your fault. And you never told on anybody. You're the kindest person I've ever known. That makes a good teacher."

"You're crazy," Sam said, "but I like you anyhow."

He was a long time getting to sleep. What was going to happen? He'd have to go through with it. He'd have to find a place for his school and get it ready to teach in. Then what would happen? Maybe six children would come. Maybe not that many. People would laugh him out of Maryville.

He found a log cabin on a farm five miles east of Maryville. He worked "from can-see to can't-see" getting it ready. He was glad to have to work hard. It was the only time he could forget the cold lump in his stomach. Sometimes even working hard didn't help.

At last the day came for school to open. He sat alone in the cabin and waited.

Hoofbeats! Wagon wheels! He jumped to his feet. Maybe a whole wagonload of children was coming!

He grinned and hurried to the door. He looked out.

Boze Hollis sat there in an empty wagon. "Just came to see you get started, Mr. Indian!"

Sam could feel the smile growing stiff on his face.

"Haw, haw! Fooled you, didn't I, Mr. Indian? You thought it was pupils coming, didn't you? Haw, haw! I wish you could see your face!"

War!

"Thought it was a wagonload of younguns, didn't you?" Boze's laughter brayed.

Two boys rode up on horseback. They eyed Boze warily.

Then a wagon came with six children. The biggest boy called, "We're in time, huh? I thought we'd better be! A lot are coming! Bet you have to turn some away, Mr. Houston!"

Mr. Houston! Nobody had ever called him that before. Sam knew his grin was stretching ear to ear.

Boze had stopped laughing. He picked up his reins and lashed at his horse. He turned his wagon so sharply that he cramped the wheels and almost upset. He drove away.

One of the boys on horseback said, "I'm glad he isn't going to your school, Mr. Houston. He's mean."

"Don't worry about the likes of Boze Hollis," Sam told him. "He wouldn't last long. Just till I had another one like him."

"What for?"

"So I could pick one up and knock the other one down with him."

The children in the wagon giggled. The littlest girl reached out to Sam. "Help me!" As he lifted her from the wagon she grabbed his ears, bumped her head against his, and beamed. "You're *nice!*"

Before time for school to begin every bench was full. Sam wasn't much of a mathematician, but he could add this up. When school ended, his debt would be paid!

More children came. Sam had to turn them away. "I'm sorry, but I can't manage any more. Not unless"— he scratched his head and studied the children solemnly —"not unless I stack them all up out in the yard—like cordwood, and bring in half of them at a time. Every other day, turn about."

A father chuckled. "You're all right, Mr. Houston. Maybe next year my younguns can go to school to you."

"Not a chance of it!" Sam thought. "When my debt is paid, I'll be back at Hiwassee! I'll feel like a man out of prison!"

But school was more fun than he had dreamed it could be. Nobody to give him orders. Everybody taking orders. Nobody causing trouble. He never kept anybody in. Never!

Long lunch hours when they walked through the woods nearby and he taught them Indian lore. Long hours after school with any children who did not have to hurry away to get home before dark. He talked with them and said poetry to them.

School was all right!

One morning before school began he looked up to see

War!

Blue Feather and The Singer in the doorway. "My brothers!"

They had brought his musket and his books.

"Does a cloud hang over The Raven?" The Singer asked.

"No. . . ." Sam tried to explain why school was fun.

The children began to arrive. They stared, big-eyed, at the Indians. Of course they had seen Indians. But not in a schoolroom! And not smiling!

"These are my brothers. I have told you about them," Sam said. "This is Blue Feather." The children smiled at him. "And this is The Singer."

The children clapped. "Oh, sing us a song! Make up a song!"

The Singer smiled. He began to chant:

> The Raven comes and the sun shines.
> The Raven goes and a cloud hangs.
> Where The Raven is—there is laughter.
> Where The Raven is not—there are long faces.
> The Raven is here and children laugh.
> But sad is his home in Hiwassee!
> Children cry. Ooooooooow!

Some of the children giggled at the howl, but others looked solemn. The Singer howled more dolefully until almost everybody laughed.

> The wolf howls! Oooooooow!
> The dog howls! Oooooooooooow!
> The owl howls! Whoooooooooo!

The littlest girl puckered up her face. "I don't like for *anybody* to be sad!"

"I shall sing you a better song!" he promised. He looked at Sam, and for once his eyes were not full of mischief. He began to chant:

> The Raven comes and the sun shines.
> The Raven goes and a cloud hangs.
> But people thank the Great Spirit!
> He who knew The Raven for many sleeps—
> He who knew The Raven for many snows—
> He thanks the Great Spirit.
> He who knew The Raven remembers.
> Every day he looks at the sky.
> Every day he says in his prayers
> "The Raven may come again!"

Silence. The Singer bowed and went out. Blue Feather followed him. Sam went with Blue Feather.

"It was a true song," The Singer said.

"Thank you. And The Raven will come again," Sam promised. "When his debt is paid."

But that summer the War of 1812 began. Sam sent a message to Hiwassee. His country was in danger. He could not come until the war was over. He was the son of a soldier. He had a debt to his country, too.

Then, as he heard talk of the war, he walked the floor and fumed. If only he could go now! But he could not. He had bargained to finish the term. By then the war would all be over. Mr. Weber said it wouldn't last three months.

When men gathered in his store, Mr. Weber told them just how it would go. "Yes, sir! All be over in three months! First, we'll make a quick dash into Canada. Drive the redcoats out of there. The Canadians will join up with us. Yes, sir! The Stars and Stripes will fly from New Orleans to the North Pole! Yes, sir! All over in three months!"

But the war wasn't over in three months. And a quick dash into Canada did not "drive the redcoats out." The Americans were driven back. They were getting beaten! The government called for more volunteers. Men did not answer the call. The government called on the militia—the home guards of the states. That did not work any better. The militiamen were ready to protect their own territory, but they were not about to leave their states and take orders from "regulars." They did not think much of regulars.

Two soldiers who had gone from Maryville came home. What a way to fight a war! No supplies. Short rations. No real commanders. Everything every which-a-way. They'd had enough of it—till they found a commander who was really going to fight. Then they'd join up again. But they'd had enough of sitting around, waiting for something to happen.

At harvest time Sam's school was through for the winter. He had paid his debt. Now he could join the army—if he could find an army that was fighting. He listened to all news and tried to decide which regiments were really doing something. But the news was confused and confusing—except that it all seemed to be bad.

One morning the next March he rode into Maryville and saw a crowd gathered in the street. He heard a fife and drum. He swung from his saddle and tossed his reins over a hitching post. "What's going on?"

"Bunch of regulars come to town," a man said. He spit in the mud to say what he thought of regulars. "Trying to get men to join up."

Sam's heart hammered. Here was his chance! "You going to join?"

The man stared. "Me? Fight with strangers? Take orders from a man I don't even know—that I didn't even elect to be my captain? Not me!"

Sam joined the crowd. He did not have any trouble seeing over men's heads. A group of regulars from the United States Army were drilling. Sam looked at their smart white trousers, their blue coats, crossed white belts, and tall shakos.

"With one of those caps," he thought, "I'd look eight feet tall!"

The sergeant gave command. The drilling stopped. The drummer set his drum on the ground, its head up. The sergeant poured a little mound of silver dollars on the drumhead.

"Who'll be the first to join his country's Army?" he

shouted. "A real army! Regular pay! Uniforms! Step right up and take a dollar from the drum! Who'll be first?"

Sam elbowed through the crowd and took a silver dollar from the drum. He had joined the regulars—joined as a common soldier.

"No, Sam!" someone yelled. "You can't do that! Not you! Not the son of a major!"

Sam laughed and looked around at the ring of faces. Nobody smiled back. What was the matter with them? Looking at him like he was a traitor.

"I'd rather be a good soldier than a poor officer!" he said. No answer. Just those blank faces. He stuck out his chin. "Just wait! Before this war ends, you'll hear of me!"

"His poor mother," a man said. "It'll break her heart."

Sam laughed, but a sinking feeling hit the pit of his stomach. What would she say?

It was an hour before he started home. He managed to think of half a dozen things he needed to see about. When he finally got home he wished he had not dawdled on the way. Mr. Jones, a neighbor, was there ahead of him. Sam could hear him.

"Joined the ranks, Mrs. Houston! The ranks! What a thing for a son of Major Houston to do! A disgrace to his father!"

Sam went in.

"Finally got here, did you?" Mr. Jones said. "What you been doing? Working up the nerve to face your mother?"

Sam did not answer.

Mother looked up. "It is true, Sam?"

"Yes, Mother. I've joined the regulars. Joined the ranks. Just a common soldier."

Silence. She sat looking up at the musket over the fireplace—Father's musket.

Mr. Jones said, "Mrs. Houston, you're not going to—"

She got up. She took the musket from the wall. She stood a moment, smoothing the polished wood of the stock, a faraway look in her eyes. Then she held it out.

"Here, Sam. Never disgrace it. Remember, I had rather all my sons filled one honorable grave than that one of them should turn his back to save his life. And remember this, Sam. The door of my cottage is always open to brave men, but it is eternally shut to cowards." She turned. "Yes, Mr. Jones? You were saying?"

"Er—nothing, ma'am." He sidled out the door. "Nothing at all, ma'am."

She smiled as she watched him go. Then she looked at Sam. "Sam, dear. I pray God spares you and sends you back to me."

He hugged her until he thought his voice was steady. "Don't worry! I'll probably come back a major! Maybe even a colonel! With medals!"

And Private Sam Houston marched away, dreaming

War!

of leading a charge against the redcoats—of taking ten prisoners single-handed—of being decorated by a general. A month or so of drilling and then . . .

A year later Sam sat on his bunk in camp, cleaning his musket and scowling. A whole year of nothing but drill, drill, drill! He hadn't been within a hundred miles of a battle! What a way to fight a war!

The officers over him said he was doing fine—had the stuff of a soldier—all that. He'd been made a drill sergeant before one could say "Charge the gun emplacements." After all, he had learned to read out of Father's *Manual of Arms*. And he had a good parade-ground bellow. Now he was Ensign Houston, in charge of a platoon. *But when would he get to fight?*

"A soldier has to be ready," Father had said. "He has to stay ready. Sometimes he has to wait."

"And how much longer," Sam muttered, "do I have to wait?"

Ben Moore, in Sam's platoon, hurried in. "Sir, have you heard the news? We're moving out tomorrow! Going to fight under General Jackson!"

"Hooray!" Sam jumped up and thumped Ben on the back. Now they'd see some action! Andrew Jackson was a real fighter! "Tough as hickory" his men said. That was why they called him Old Hickory—behind his back. He was famous for two things—his courage and his temper.

Old Hickory's boys, the militia of West Tennessee,

had been in the fight from the beginning. Sam didn't know where they had been or where they were now—news was slow reaching camp—but it was enough to know they'd be serving under Jackson. Funny, too. Regulars going to serve under a commander of militia.

"Hooray!" Sam said again. "Now we'll lick the redcoats!"

"Not the 'redcoats,' sir," Ben said. "The 'redskins.' We're going to be fighting Indians." He hurried out to spread the news.

Indians! Sam's fingers shook as he picked up his musket. He tried three times to ram the swab down the barrel and missed it.

Indians! The Cherokees? For years the Americans had been edging in on the Cherokee lands. Making treaties—each one "the last and final treaty"—then breaking them.

Oo-loo-te-ka had said he lived at peace. But he was just one Cherokee chief. There were dozens of them—maybe hundreds. What of the others? Were they siding with the British? And if they were, what would Oo-loo-te-ka do?

Sam had a hollow place where his heart belonged. What if he had to face Blue Feather in battle?

A soldier obeys.

He did not sleep that night.

Horseshoe Bend

He got up the next morning with a cold lump in his stomach. The camp bristled with preparations for the march.

Lieutenant Marsden called together the officers who served under him.

"You will keep your men together on the march!" he said sternly. "No straggling! Understand? *No straggling!* Even with our Cherokee scouts riding ahead—"

"Cherokees! *Our* scouts!" Sam blurted out the words.

A shocked silence fell. No one ever interrupted a superior when he was speaking.

Mr. Marsden stared coldly. "Yes, Mr. Houston," he said with icy precision. "*Our* scouts. We'll need scouts. Without them, we might march straight into an ambush of Creek Indians. And Red Eagle's braves might give us a taste of what they did to Fort Mims. Do you know what happened there, Mr. Houston? Lookouts failed to keep watch. Red Eagle took the fort. His warriors butchered every man, woman, and child. Would you like to lead your men into an ambush of Creek warriors, Mr. Houston?"

"No, sir. I—" But how could he explain?

"Then be glad we have Cherokee scouts, Mr. Houston."

"Yes, sir!" *You don't know how glad!* Sam thought. The cold lump in his stomach went away.

Soon the regiment was on the march. Sam's feet beat out the words: "Not against the Cherokees. Not against the Cherokees."

But that night other words haunted him. What if you *did* have to fight against friends? *A soldier obeys!*

Day after day they tramped through the wilderness. Silent, wary, eyes flicking left and right. Even with the Cherokee scouts riding ahead, who knew what might be lurking behind any tree?

At last they joined General Jackson and the two thousand men of the West Tennessee militia. Old Hickory's men weren't in uniform. They wore buckskin, homespun, linsey-woolsey and hand-me-downs. But they swaggered as they walked and they looked over the "regulars" with scorn in their eyes.

The 39th Regiment stood at attention as Old Hickory rode by. He looked too sick to sit in his saddle. One arm was in a sling. He'd been wounded in a duel, someone said. Yes, Old Hickory had a temper.

He recognized young Major Montgomery of the regulars and paused to speak to him. Sam was near enough to hear their words.

"So they've sent me some regulars, eh?"

"Yes, sir."

"And how have they armed the pride of the United States Army?" Old Hickory asked. "With rifles, I hope."

"No, sir. Just with smooth bores."

"Humph. Useless for long range. Good thing I can depend on my Tennessee boys for real marksmanship, isn't it?"

Major Montgomery flushed and said quietly, "Yes, sir."

"Why the devil do they send me men armed with smooth bores?"

"Maybe they knew the trained soldiers would stick, sir. Obey orders, and stick to the end."

For a moment Old Hickory's eyes flashed in his white face. It looked as though there might be another duel in the making. Then he smiled. "Maybe that's it, my boy! Maybe that's it! Lord knows I can do with some men who stick! My Tennessee boys are all right. But the volunteers I've had—bah!"

Soon they were tramping through forests again. On March 26 they camped near a bend in the Tallapoosa River.

That night Major Montgomery talked to his officers—even the sergeants and ensigns.

"I thought you gentlemen would all like to understand the situation," he said. As he talked he sketched. "Here is a great bend in the Tallapoosa. Called Horse-

shoe Bend. You can see why. Here to the north the opening is very narrow."

He pointed out the spot. "Red Eagle has thrown up a
barricade of logs across this opening. All around him,
east, west, and south, the river is deep enough to protect
him. Our only way of attack is from the north. He has
about a thousand warriors. General Jackson has warned
him—told him to send away all women and children.
It'll be a fight to the end. If we can make a breach in the
barricade with our cannons—"

"And if we—" The young sergeant stopped and red-
dened. "I beg your pardon, sir."

Major Montgomery looked up slowly. He smiled at
the embarrassed sergeant. There was a reason why he
was the most popular man in the 39th. "If we can't
smash the barricade, we'll charge. We'll go over it.
We've got to win this battle!" He stood. He shook hands
with every man.

Sam had a tingle down his spine. He knew he was not
the only man who felt that way. Every mother's son of
them would give his right arm for the major. Or maybe
his left arm—so he could go on fighting!

At ten-thirty the next morning the bombardment of
the barricade began. The troops stood in battle forma-
tion, waiting . . . and waiting.

An hour passed. Not a break in the barricade. The
cannon balls buried themselves in the logs. That was all.

Sam muttered to himself. "How much longer?"

Horseshoe Bend

Major Montgomery walked past, checking his men. A word here, a smile there. He seemed to read Sam's thoughts. He said, "General Coffee has taken his men around to the south of the bend, to cut off any retreat. When we know he's in position, we'll charge."

Another hour dragged by. Then a Cherokee scout came riding pell-mell with a paper for General Jackson. Old Hickory read it and smiled.

"General Coffee's south of them, all right," he said. "And he's done better than that!" He beamed at the Cherokee. "Know what our Cherokee scouts did? Spotted canoes across the river, where the Creeks had hidden them, ready for retreat. Be hanged if those Cherokees didn't swim under water, like so many eels, cross the river, and bring back every canoe! Without rousing a single Creek!"

"Yes," Sam thought, "the Cherokees can swim under water! I found that out!"

"Now General Coffee's got his crack riflemen across the river, in the rear of Red Eagle's camp." Old Hickory spoke to the scout. "Tell him we're ready. When he starts his attack, we charge!"

The Cherokee raced away. Sam smiled. Friends and allies! Fighting with us! Again the thought stirred. What if they had been enemies? *A soldier obeys!*

Presently they heard the distant crack of rifles. The men before the barricade stiffened. The drums beat the long roll.

Major Montgomery shouted "Fo-o-o-orward!" and led the charge.

Sam started behind the major, but he was almost even with him when the major mounted the barricade. Behind the logs a rifle cracked. The major fell, a black hole in his forehead.

Sam gave one yell of rage. Sword in hand, he scrambled to the top of the barricade. Something hit his left thigh with the kick of a mule. He leaped down among the Indians, slashing right and left with his sword.

Other men leaped down and joined the fight. Gradually the Creeks retreated from the barricade. They hid behind trees and rocks, in gullies, behind other barricades of logs, and went on fighting. It might take all day, Sam knew, to rout them out of every hiding place. It was quiet around the first barricade now. The fighting had moved on.

A soldier said, "Sir, you're wounded!"

Sam remembered the mule kick in his thigh. He looked down. A feathered arrow was sticking out of his leg. He grabbed it and gave one quick jerk. That was the way to do it. One quick jerk. But the "one quick jerk" did not bring the arrow. Barbed. It would hang in there like a fishhook! The ground began to spin.

He spoke to the soldier. "Pull it out."

"Yes, sir!" The soldier tried. He stopped. He turned white. "I—I can't sir!"

Sam lifted his sword, "Pull it out!"

The soldier gulped, wet his lips, grabbed the arrow, shut his eyes, and jerked. The barbed head tore a hole in Sam's leg. Blood spurted.

"Sir, we've got to get that bandaged, or you'll bleed to death!" He helped Sam over the barricade.

Sam steadied himself a moment against the logs, then started to walk.

A sergeant grabbed his arm. "Wait! You idiot! You want to bleed to death . . . *sir!*"

"I'm all right." But Sam was glad there was a tree he could lean against as he slid to the ground.

The sergeant slapped a thick pad over the wound and tied it tight enough to stop the bleeding.

"Thanks." Sam pulled himself to his feet and started again toward the barricade.

Behind him a voice barked, "You there! To the rear!"

"Not me!" Sam yelled. "Who's trying to tell me what—" He turned and gasped. It was General Jackson.

Sam stiffened and saluted. "I'm all right now, sir. Just a—"

"You heard me! To the rear!"

Sam saluted again. He tried to about-face smartly, but staggered and grabbed the general's saddle to steady himself. "I—I beg your pardon, sir!"

Old Hickory glared, then grinned. "What's your name, my bellowing young upstart?"

"Sam Houston, sir."

"Related to Major Sam Houston of Timber Ridge?"

"He was my father, sir."

"You have a proud name, my boy. And I like your spirit. Even if you don't have good sense. Now, to the rear. And stay there!"

"Yes . . . sir. . . ." The ground was really spinning now.

Two men helped Sam to the rear. He lay on the ground. His leg began to throb. The sound of battle faded—became louder—and faded again.

He must have slept. When he opened his eyes the sun was about three o'clock high. He pulled himself to his feet and limped toward the fight. The barricade had been torn down. He picked his way through the logs.

The guns were silent. Old Hickory was staring toward one last barricade, built over a narrow ravine. "We can't bring our cannon to bear on it," he said. "Anyhow, it's a pity to go on killing."

He sent an officer with a white flag. "Tell them if they surrender they'll be treated as prisoners of war." He added through his teeth, "We'll not murder them as they did the woman and children of Fort Mims!"

The officer reached the barricade. He delivered the message. He started back. A defiant yell rose from behind the logs. A bullet ripped the white flag. Another bullet—and the officer fell.

Old Hickory's face went white with rage. "Then they

die!" For a moment he eyed the barricade. "We've got to take it by assault. I'll not order men to rush that barricade. I'll ask for volunteers."

Sam waited for the yell and the charge. In the confusion Old Hickory would not notice him—would not know that he had disobeyed orders. But not a man moved. Sam grabbed a musket from the nearest man.

"Follow me!" He started down the slope.

He was within five yards of the barricade when a bullet hit his right shoulder. Another hit his right arm. The musket fell from his hand. He dropped to his belly, crawled out of range of the bullets, and lay still.

When he opened his eyes it was dark. A man stood over him with a flickering pine torch. It felt as though a red-hot poker jabbed his shoulder.

"How about it, Doc?" the man asked.

"No use digging for the other bullet," the doctor said. "No use to torture him. He won't last the night. Lost too much blood."

"A Soldier Obeys!"

Sam closed his eyes. Nobody seemed to know he was conscious.

The doctor said, "Set his arm. Might as well make him comfortable as possible till he goes."

Two men grabbed the arm, jerked, and slapped it into splints. They left him on the ground and went their way. They had work to do with men who might live.

"I won't die! I won't die!" Sam gritted his teeth. He tried to stay awake, to hold on to life that way.

But he finally slept. When he wakened it was morning.

He heard the doctor's voice. "Confound it, General Jackson, I don't know why he's still alive, but he is."

"Maybe," Old Hickory said, "the good Lord still has something for him to do. Take him to Fort Williams."

"Sixty miles on a horse litter?" the doctor said. "He'll die on the way. Too bad he didn't go last night."

He dressed the shoulder wound again and the wound in Sam's leg. Men heaved Sam onto a stretcher between two horses. The long jouncing miles began. Sometimes

"A Soldier Obeys!"

Sam thought the doctor had been right. It would have been easier to have died when he was lying still. *But he wouldn't die!*

Each morning Sam heard someone say, "He's still hanging on."

Fort Williams at last.

Day after day he lay on a straw-stuffed tick on the floor. One by one the other wounded men died or recovered.

Every morning someone looked at Sam and said, "*Still* hanging on."

Late in May—more than two months after the battle of Horseshoe Bend—a horse litter jounced up the rough trail to Sam's home. Two soldiers carried him to the door.

Sam heard his mother's voice, "Can I help you?"

He opened his eyes. "Is the door . . . of your cottage . . . open to me?"

"Sam! Oh, Sam!"

"It's been a hard journey, ma'am," one of the soldiers said. "But he wanted to see you again before he—I mean while he—I mean—"

Mother lifted her chin. "Are you trying to say that Sam is dying? You don't know Sam! He'll be ready to lick the both of you in three weeks!"

But three weeks later Sam still lay flat on a bed. Mother was always smiling when she sat by him. Once, though, when she did not know he was awake, he saw her hide her face in her hands.

Finally she took him to a doctor in Knoxville.

The doctor shook his head. "No, ma'am, I won't try to doctor him. He's not going to last the week. It'd be a shame to take your money."

Sam stayed in Knoxville.

Ten days later he was still alive. He even seemed to be a little stronger. The doctor threw up his hands. "All right! All right! I'll do what I can for you! But I don't know why you're still alive!"

"Old Hickory said . . . maybe the good Lord still had . . . something for me to . . . do."

At last Sam was well enough to go home.

"You're definitely on the mend," Mother said one day. "You're getting grouchy as a bear with a sore head. I remember what my grandmother always said: 'An ornery disposition is a good sign in a sick man.' "

Sam tried to smile. "I'm sorry, Mother. But, confound it, I want to get back into service! If I don't, the Army will pitch me out!"

"And you want to stay in the Army, Sam?"

"More than anything! You're sorry?"

"No, Sam. Your father left you a proud name. You'll live up to it."

"I have something else to live up to. What you said when I marched away. *I'll never turn my back to save my life.*"

"A Soldier Obeys!"

A neighbor brought a letter for Sam. "It's from the War Department!" he said.

Sam's heart lurched. They were dismissing him. "Thanks for your trouble. Just lay it there."

The neighbor shuffled his feet. "Aren't you going to open it?"

"I might as well," Sam thought. "Everybody will know sooner or later." He broke the seal. He started to read, then shouted. "Mother! They didn't dismiss me! I'm Second Lieutenant Houston now!"

There was a personal note from General Jackson, too, written in his own hand! Sam was to have unlimited furlough until he was fit for service. When he was ready, there would be a place for him!

The neighbor beamed. "Congratulations! Second lieutenant! *And* a letter from General Jackson! Just wait till I tell folks about that! Guess they'll stop saying—" He flushed. "You know how people talk." He hurried out.

Old Hickory remembered him! Sam felt his grin spreading.

"That ought to improve your disposition," Mother said.

Sam laughed with her.

Nothing could "improve his disposition," though, when he heard of the burning of Washington.

The British had sailed into Chesapeake Bay and marched toward the city. An American force of raw

61

recruits had tried to stand them off. But at the first volley the Americans broke and ran. The British marched on the capital and burned it.

Sam could not believe it! A few men might panic. But not a whole regiment! But they had. One newspaper wit called the panic-stricken flight "the Bladensburg races."

It was not until January of 1815 that Sam heard news that wiped out the shame of "the Bladensburg races." Old Hickory had done it again! General Jackson—of the U.S. Army now—had trounced the British at New Orleans! Over two thousand British lost in the battle— only a handful of Americans. That was the kind of news he liked!

Soon that news turned to ashes, too. It had been a useless battle. Peace had been signed in Ghent, Belgium, two weeks before the battle of New Orleans.

"Two thousand men killed for nothing," a man said. "If you ask me, the whole blasted war was for nothing! What did we gain by it? Look at you, Sam! What good did it do for you to get shot up at Horseshoe Bend? And what'll become of you now? The war's over. They're dismissing men right and left. They'll throw you out in a hurry. Then what'll you do?"

Sam didn't answer. He was asking himself the same question. What would become of him? He heard that his entire regiment, the 39th, was being disbanded. So . . . that was that. Every day he watched for a letter from the War Department.

"A Soldier Obeys!"

It came. Dismissal? He opened it slowly. *No!*

Sam was transferred to the 1st Infantry, stationed in New Orleans. He would report there when he was ready for duty.

He still had the bandage on his shoulder when he went to New Orleans. He tried to keep anybody from knowing about the wound that had never healed. But one day a brother officer gave him a terrific whack on the shoulder. Sam swore. The truth came out.

"We're taking you to Dr. Kerr!" his commanding officer said. "Best surgeon in the Army!"

Dr. Kerr looked too young to be "the best surgeon in the Army," but Sam liked him.

The doctor examined the shoulder, then came straight to the point. "I can operate. I can try to get that bullet. But—it's going to be a risk. Frankly, it may be safer to go on the way you are."

"With a hole in my shoulder that won't heal?"

"Exactly."

"And if you operate, it will heal?"

"I can't promise that. I can promise that it's a risk." He turned away, messing with his instruments. "So, make up your mind."

"I already have. Go to it!"

"Who is your next of kin?"

"My mother."

"I want you to write her a letter."

Sam cocked an eyebrow. "In case I didn't pull through?"

"Exactly."

"Well, I'll write it, but it's going to be a waste of paper."

"Cocky young whelp, aren't you?"

Sam grinned. "Old Hickory called me a 'bellowing young upstart.' "

The doctor sent for two husky men to hold Sam still, gave him a good slug of whiskey, and went to work.

Later—Sam didn't know whether it was minutes, hours, or days—he looked up and saw the blur of a face bending over him. "Dr. Kerr?"

"Right here."

"Wasted . . . that letter . . . didn't I?"

"It was a close call, my friend."

"How soon will it heal?"

"Maybe never. Can't tell yet."

"Can I stay in the Army?"

"That's up to you."

"Then I stay."

"Doing what?"

"Whatever my country needs me to do. I remember what my father said once: 'A soldier obeys.' "

Late in 1817 Sam was on duty in Nashville. Paper work. Dull . . . dull . . . dull. . . .

He spent his free time reading records of battles, studying maps, figuring out the why of troop movements. His brother officers twitted him. What was he getting ready for? Another war? Not much chance of that! Americans had had their bellies full with the last one!

In October a major sent for Sam.

He marched to the office and saluted. "Lieutenant Houston reporting, sir."

The major was cordial. "Oh, yes, Mr. Houston! We have a special assignment for you."

Good! Anything was better than paper work!

"General Jackson seems to put a lot of confidence in you."

Old Hickory still remembered him! Sam wanted to grin like a fool, but he kept a straight face and eyes front.

"We have a very—er—delicate mission. General Jackson says you're the man who can help handle it. You're the young rebel who ran off and lived with the Indians for three years, aren't you?"

"Yes, sir."

"You know the Creek Indians gave up a lot of land in Alabama. . . ."

"Served them right, sir!" Sam said. "After what they did at Fort Mims!"

"Yes, yes, quite so," the major said quickly. "And our government has been dealing with the Cherokees, too. We've made treaties with them. But now some of the chiefs are refusing to honor the treaties."

"They signed treaties and now won't honor them,

sir?" Sam asked. "It doesn't sound like the Cherokees I've known, sir."

"Certain chiefs signed the treaties for all of them. But now some of the other chiefs are refusing to sell their lands and move west. This is where General Jackson says you'll be invaluable."

Sam's heart began to hammer.

"Of course, we could send in a regiment or two and *make* them go. But that would mean bloodshed. We don't want that. You'll go as subagent. To prevent tragedy and bloodshed. To keep the peace. Persuade the Indians it's the best thing to do."

Sam wet his lips. "Where do I go, sir?"

"Oh, didn't I tell you? To Hiwassee Island."

"A Disgrace
to the Army!"

"I won't do it! I won't do it!" Sam wanted to shout the words. Instead he saluted, wheeled, and marched from the office. *A soldier obeys.* . . . He reported to the Army doctor.

"I'm going to be away for a while. I'll need stuff to take care of my shoulder."

"Where?" The doctor listened and pounded his desk. "No! Absolutely not! You've no business on duty like that! If they insist on that duty, I'll order you furloughed until this business with the Cherokees is over!"

A way out. . . . A chance to refuse the duty. . . . Sam almost said, "Yes, sir," But—if he didn't go—what would happen to Oo-loo-te-ka and his people?

"I'm going, sir. I'll appreciate it if you can help me."

The next day, clad in buckskins, Sam set out for Hi-wassee.

The young children in the village did not know him, but an old man knew him instantly. Sam heard the word spreading: "The Raven has come! The Raven has come home!"

Oo-loo-te-ka met him with outstretched hands. "My son! Five winters have passed since we said good-by. We have heard that The Raven is brave in battle! My young braves were proud to fight in the army with The Raven!"

Sam tried to answer, but the words stuck in his throat.

That night, after they had eaten, the chief said, "A cloud hangs over my son."

Sam told him why he had come. "My heart is heavy. But some chiefs of the Cherokees did make paper talk. These chiefs swore they made paper talk for you, too."

"No. And I did not make paper talk. I did not promise to sell my land. It was the land of my father's fathers. It will be the land of my children's children. I did not promise to sell it!"

"These chiefs said they spoke for all of you."

"I do not understand the ways of the Great White Father," Oo-loo-te-ka said. "In the war, the Creeks fought with your enemies. They burned and killed. Your General Jackson defeated them. He took their lands. That is right. They were enemies. But we were friends. We fought with your General Jackson. Why does the Great White Father take our lands?"

"He is not taking your land," Sam told him. "He is buying it. He will pay for it. He will help you move beyond the Mississippi—the Father of Waters. There you will live in peace forever. The white man will never come."

"But I do not want to leave my home!"

"My father, it is a dark day. But it will be a darker day if you do not go."

"The Great White Father will send his soldiers? He will kill the Cherokees who were his friends? I see. . . ." For a long time Oo-loo-te-ka was silent. "So . . . I wonder how it is with my brother, Tah-lhon-tuskey? Ten winters have passed since he made paper talk with the white man. He went beyond the Father of Waters. He thought his people would be happier away from the white man. He did not like what was happening to his young braves. The fire water of the white man—it is bad medicine for the Indian."

"Fire water doesn't do the white man any good, either," Sam said.

"It is more bad medicine for the Indian," the chief said. "So my brother Tah-lhon-tuskey left the world of the white man. But I do not want to go! I do not know why I am being driven from my land!" He looked at Sam. "And why has my son come with this message? Is he to make us go?"

"I am to stay with you. To help you get ready for the journey. To see that you have everything the Great White Father promised you in the paper talk."

"To see that we get good dealing? Justice?"

Sam's face burned. "My father, I cannot undo what has been done. I can only try to help."

"So . . ." Oo-loo-te-ka sighed. "I must make my people understand."

"I hope you can!" Sam thought. "I'd hate to have to do it!"

He went out of Oo-loo-te-ka's cabin and came face to face with Blue Feather.

"My brother!" Blue Feather's eyes were shining.

"I might as well get it over with," Sam thought.

Blue Feather listened. His eyes were cold now. "May the Great Spirit pity you!" he said. "He who walks with the white man cannot walk a straight path." He wheeled and left Sam alone.

Sam felt sick at his stomach. He heard the summons and watched the people go to the council hall. He walked in the other direction and sat under a tree with his head on his knees. He'd have to be here for weeks, the major had said. Every day he'd have to face Blue Feather's scorn.

The meeting ended. He saw the silent figures going to their cabins. Not a word. . . .

Then Blue Feather came and stood by him. "Our brother is weary. Come. My wigwam is yours. Tomorrow, Blue Feather hunts. Is The Raven's eye still true? Do his arrows wing to their mark?"

The sick feeling in Sam's stomach melted, but there was a lump in his throat. "The Raven is weak," he said. "His arm is not strong. But he shall go with you."

"A Disgrace to the Army!"

Day after day they roamed the woods. Sometimes they brought back game. One day two other young braves went with them. They stopped once on a steep bank above a trail.

Suddenly from below they heard the crack of a whip and a loud cry. Sam looked down on the trail. Two white men, on horseback, were leading two pack mules. In front of them they were driving ten Negroes, roped one behind the other. The chunky gray-bearded man carried a musket. The lanky redhead had a long whip. One of the black men had fallen. Streaks across his back oozed blood. He tried to get up, but fell again.

Slave runners! Sam had heard of them. Ever since the United States had outlawed importing more slaves, there had been slave smugglers. They brought Negroes from Spanish possessions or from Africa and landed them on the Gulf Coast. They smuggled them through the forests to men who were willing to pay and no questions asked.

Just as Sam looked down, the redhead cursed and raised his whip.

The graybeard said, "No use. We'll have to cut him out of the string and leave him."

"What if someone finds him?"

"He won't be talking," the graybeard said.

Sam motioned to the Indians for silence, then whispered. They nodded. Sam leaped, landed on the back of the graybeard, tumbled him from his horse, and grabbed his musket.

The redhead whirled. "Why, you dirty stinking savage! You—"

Sam stepped back, covering them both with the musket. "I am Lieutenant Houston of the United States Army, on special assignment to the Cherokee Indians!"

The smugglers looked at each other.

The redhead managed a weak smile. "All right, all right, soldier! How much do you want?"

"What do you mean?"

"Don't act dumb. How much do you make in six months? We'll double it. We've greased palms a lot higher up than a scurvy lieutenant's."

Sam whistled. Three brown bodies leaped. A momentary tussle, and the smugglers stood helpless, with their arms twisted behind them.

Blue Feather had the redhead's whip. "What now, my brother?"

"Take their pack mules and their slaves. Let them have their horses."

The redhead bellowed, "You can't do this! I'll have you ruined! I'll—"

Sam nodded. Blue Feather lifted his bow. An arrow whistled over the graybeard's head.

"Next time," Sam said, "he'll aim closer. Better start riding."

The redhead whined. "But you can't send us off without food! Without a gun! Without—"

An arrow whistled past his ear.

"A Disgrace to the Army!"

The smugglers jumped on their horses and fled.

Blue Feather smiled. "Now what, my brother?"

Sam scratched his head. He looked at the slaves. "That's a good question. What the devil *will* I do with them?"

Ten days later two Cherokees entered Maryville with a note for the sheriff of Blount County:

> Dear sir
>
> I am sending you these ten slaves which I took from smugglers. You will know what to do with them.
>
> Will you please sign the receipt for their delivery, so I will know that the Indians were true to their trust?
>
> > Your obedient servant
> > Sam Houston
> > 1st Lt. U.S.A.

Two times after that smugglers met Sam, tried to bribe him, and lost their pack mules and their slaves. Then no more smugglers appeared in the region.

"Word must have gotten around," Sam remarked. "Maybe word will even travel up to high places. That first redhead said they had greased palms higher up than a scurvy lieutenant's."

"Can the mighty ones send bolts of lightning on our brother?" Blue Feather asked.

"How?" Sam asked. "They'd have to admit they were

73

helping men break the law. They can't do a thing. But I wish they'd try!" He added through his teeth, "I'd like to meet one face to face!"

"My brother is strange," Blue Feather said. "His people have owned slaves."

"We never treated one the way the smugglers treat those poor devils!"

"Sometimes," Blue Feather said thoughtfully, "I have been very savage in a fight. Sometimes . . . when I was angry with myself."

Sam's face burned. Had he been "very savage in the fight" against the smugglers because of his shame? His shame over what he was helping his government do to these Indians? Just because some Cherokee chiefs had been frightened—or bribed—into signing away land that was not theirs? He'd be glad when this duty was over.

In January of 1818 Sam got back to Nashville. He winced as he stripped off his buckskins. His shoulder was kicking up again. The doctor was going to raise Cain.

He laid out his uniform and stood looking down at it. *A soldier obeys.* Well, he had carried out orders. Oo-loo-te-ka and his people were on their way west. They had gone without bloodshed. Maybe they'd like their new home. He wished he could think so.

He washed, dressed in his uniform, and went to report.

"A Disgrace to the Army!"

The major beamed. "Mission accomplished, eh, Mr. Houston?"

"Yes, sir." Sam spoke with careful politeness. "Oo-loo-te-ka has honored a treaty he did not sign and has left the land of his fathers."

The major glanced up. His eyes narrowed. "You're looking a little the worse for wear, Mr. Houston. Your shoulder bothering you?"

"Not as much as my stomach!" Sam thought. "Sometimes I'm sick at my stomach when I think about Hiwassee!" He said only, "Nothing serious, sir."

"I'll arrange a month's leave for you."

"That won't be necessary, sir."

"Nonsense, you deserve it. You know, I shouldn't be surprised if you received a promotion for this." He waited, but Sam did not speak. "Promotions aren't easy to come by in peacetime, you know. You've done very well. A first lieutenant already. How'd you like to be Captain Houston?"

"I had thought of another reward," Sam told him quietly.

"What's that?"

"Thirty pieces of silver . . . sir."

The major stiffened, then said, "That's all, Mr. Houston. Go see the doctor. That's an order. Then enjoy your leave. That's an order too."

But two days later Sam was ordered back on duty. He was to go to Knoxville, to report to Governor McNimm.

It would be well for him to take his Indian garb with him.

What in the name of heaven this time?

The governor beamed. "Come in, Sam, my boy! You're just the man I need. You were adopted into Oo-loo-te-ka's tribe, weren't you? He called you 'son'?"

"Yes, sir."

"Then, according to the Indian way of looking at things, you'd be related to his brother, wouldn't you?"

"Tah-lhon-tuskey?" Sam asked.

"You've heard of him?" The governor listened and nodded. "Yes, Tah-lhon-tuskey went west without any pressure. A very friendly arrangement. But now Tah-lhon-tuskey is here with some of his braves. On his way to Washington."

"With complaints, sir?" Sam asked.

"Er—yes. He seems to feel the government has not lived up to its promises. Very awkward, coming up just now. When we've more Cherokees to move. I've sent messengers ahead to warn Mr. Calhoun, our Secretary of War, that there is trouble in the offing. I want the old chief to have every courtesy. You know, he's quite a personality. Kingly."

"It must run in the family, sir," Sam said.

"What I want, Sam, is for you to go east with Tah-lhon-tuskey. I'm sorry to interrupt your leave, but this is important."

Sam packed his uniform, put on his buckskins, and went to meet the old chief.

"A Disgrace to the Army!"

"Co-lon-neh!" Tah-lhon-tuskey said. "The son of my brother. The Great Spirit is good to us! He has sent us a friend!"

In Washington, Secretary of War Calhoun made the Indians welcome. He was the soul of courtesy. But when the Indians had gone, he turned on Sam.

"You, sir! What do you mean—appearing before the Secretary of War in that dress? You—a member of the Army of the United States!"

Sam tried to explain, but Mr. Calhoun did not let him get a word in edgewise. Sam clenched his fists and waited for the tirade to end.

"You, sir," Mr. Calhoun finished, "are a disgrace to the Army!"

"Yes, sir." Sam bowed and walked out.

He strode, unseeing, back to the hotel. He unpacked his uniform, then hurled it on the floor. He spent hours writing blistering letters to Mr. Calhoun—and tearing them up.

The next morning a boy wakened him with a message. Mr. Houston would report to the office of the Honorable Mr. Calhoun at ten o'clock.

Sam grinned and dressed. Evidently Mr. Calhoun had cooled off. Maybe the reason for Indian dress had finally dawned on him. A good thing, Sam thought, he had not sent one of those letters he had written!

On the stroke of ten, correctly dressed in uniform, Sam entered Mr. Calhoun's office. He was ready to smile and say, "It's all forgotten, sir. No need to apologize."

Mr. Calhoun sat, frozen-faced, at his desk. Three high-ranking officers, equally frozen-faced, stared at Sam.

"Mr. Houston," Mr. Calhoun said, "you are here to answer grave charges: That, during your recent tour of duty on Hiwassee Island, you did, on sundry occasions, aid and abet slave smugglers in the vicinity of said island. Do you plead guilty or not guilty?"

Sam started to answer. To his horror, he laughed. The eyes around him grew colder.

"I beg your pardon, sir. I did, on three occasions, meet up with smugglers. But, sir, I did not aid and abet them. I took their slaves and sent them to the sheriff of Blount County."

"Why?"

"Because, sir, I did not know what the devil—begging your pardon, sir—to do with them."

"How do you account for the charge against you?"

"I have only one suggestion, sir. When the first pair of smugglers tried to bribe me, I remember what one of them said: 'We have greased palms a lot higher than a scurvy lieutenant's.' "

"You may return to quarters," Mr. Calhoun said. "You will remain in Washington until further notice."

Sam bowed himself out, more amused than angry.

The investigation dragged on for days. Sam never knew who had accused him. Once more he was called before Mr. Calhoun.

The charges against Mr. Houston had been dropped.

"A Disgrace to the Army!"

He would be ready to leave the next morning to conduct Tah-lhon-tuskey and his braves back west as far as the Hiwassee River.

That was all. No apology. No explanation. No information about who had tried to ruin him.

That night Sam wrote another letter. This one did not take long. Sam Houston, first lieutenant, was resigning from the Army.

He looked at the date on the letter: March 1, 1818. Tomorrow he would be twenty-five. What had he to show for those years?

He sat with his head in his hands. What would become of him now? An ex-Army man—in debt—with a wound that had never healed. With no training for any other career. Twenty-five—and a failure.

"Old Hickory's Boy"

Back at Hiwassee River Sam said good-by to Tah-lhon-tuskey. "You shall live always in my heart."

"And The Raven shall live always in the hearts of my people," the old chief said. "What word shall I take my brother?"

"Tell him The Raven has put the drum away. He is leaving the Army."

"What shall The Raven do?"

"He shall become a lawyer. Maybe that is the way to fight for justice!"

"How does a man become a lawyer?"

"The Raven shall go to the office of a good lawyer. He will find many books of Talking Leaves. The Raven shall study the Talking Leaves. After many moons The Raven shall face a trial. Wise men will ask many questions. If the Raven can answer, he will be a lawyer."

"The Raven must do that for many moons? He must live away from the sky and the stars?" Tah-lhon-tuskey asked. "The Raven will be sad. We shall pray to the

Great Spirit for him. Good-by, my kinsman. We shall grieve for The Raven as for a man in a dungeon."

With a hollow feeling where his stomach belonged Sam packed away his uniforms. He packed his buckskins. Two lives behind him. . . . He put on the new clothes he had bought. He had gone in debt for them.

In June he stood in the office of Mr. James Trimble of Nashville.

Old Mr. Trimble was puzzled. "But, Sam, I thought you wanted a career in the Army?"

"I have resigned, sir."

"Hmmm. And you think you want to read law?"

Sam looked at the rows of dark, heavy books that lined the walls. *We shall grieve for The Raven as for a man in a dungeon.* Sam tried to forget Tah-lhon-tuskey's eyes. "Yes, sir, I want to read law."

"It'll be a long, hard row to hoe."

"How long, sir?"

"At least a year and a half. At least that long—if you are a good student and apply yourself. What sort of student were you?"

Sam didn't go into that. "I taught school once, sir."

"That so? Bless me, I'd never have thought of you as the studious sort. You may do all right. How old are you?"

"Twenty-five, sir."

"Bless me! You're starting a new career very late! Here it is June. It'll be January of eighteen-twenty before you can possibly stand for your examinations. You'll be almost twenty-seven. Almost twenty-seven—and just ready to begin a new career."

"Yes, sir, I know. But I'm going to work hard, sir!"

"You'll need to!"

The long grind began. The days crawled by . . . the weeks . . . the months.

One morning in December Sam said, "Sir, I think I'm ready to stand for my examinations."

"What! I said a year and a half! Not half a year!"

"Will you question me, sir? See if you think I'm—"

"Oh, yes, I'll question you, my fine young friend! I'll question you till . . ." After an hour Mr. Trimble stopped. "Bless my soul! You're—you're unbelievable! You're impossible!"

"Will you recommend me to stand for my examinations?"

"With pleasure! With the greatest of pleasure!" Mr. Trimble was shaking his head, but he was smiling, too.

The next week it was all over Nashville. Sam Houston had passed his examinations for the bar after only six months of study!

Old Hickory, at The Hermitage, his home near Nashville, sent for Sam. "Well, my bellowing young upstart, I hear you've set the town by its ears. And at least two fine old firms are offering to take you in. Which one you going to join?"

"Neither one, sir. I'm going to open my own office."

"Eh? Got any money to tide you over?"

"No, sir."

"You have an interest in your father's estate, don't you?"

"I sold it to one of my brothers. But I'm still not out of debt."

"And you're going to start on your own and wait for fees?" Old Hickory chuckled. "You might make out all right! You just might! Where you going?"

Sam had heard they needed a lawyer in the little town of Lebanon, thirty miles east of Nashville. He was going there.

"Have any friends in Lebanon?"

"No, sir," Sam admitted. "I'll be on my own. . . . Completely on my own."

Old Hickory grinned. "Like the sound of that, don't you?"

Sam grinned, too. "Yes, sir, I believe I do!"

"Lebanon's not too far from here," Old Hickory said. "Ride over and see us sometimes."

"Why—thank you, sir!"

"Always room for your feet under my table—and that's a lot of room. Let's see . . . let's say about the end of January, eh? Come over then and tell me how you're doing."

"Thank you, sir!"

"Don't thank me. You're good company, you young whelp!"

Sam still had a grin on his face when he got back to Nashville. He bought himself a law library. He wished he could buy new clothes. His trousers were a little shiny from sitting. But he was already in debt.

"All right!" he told himself. "You wanted to be on your own! You are!" He set out for Lebanon.

Mr. Isaac Galladay, postmaster and owner of a general store in Lebanon, was a jolly, bustling man. "So you're the Sam Houston that made the bar in six months. Welcome to Lebanon. And now you're starting on your own. It'll be a while before you'll earn your keep, you know. How much money you have?"

"None," Sam admitted. "Less than none. I'm in debt."

"Hmmm. Well, I've got a building you can use for an office."

It was a snug log cabin with a fieldstone chimney and fireplace. It reminded Sam of his schoolhouse in Maryville, the log cabin where he'd paid his first debt of one hundred dollars. He was in debt for more than a hundred dollars now. And he'd go further in debt before he'd start collecting any fees. The rent of his office alone would . . .

"I don't approve of big debts," Mr. Galladay said sternly. "I'll charge you one dollar a month for your office."

"What!"

"Now—about postage. That's another item. High. Twenty-five cents a letter. I can let you have credit for that for a while."

"Mr. Galladay, you're—"

"But there's one place I'm going to put my foot down. You've got to have decent clothes. Got to *look* like a rising young lawyer—even before you start rising. You'll sign a note for that money."

"How can I ever thank you for—"

"Nonsense! Just protecting my investment. If I'm ever going to get that rent money out of you, you've got to succeed."

"If the rest of the town is like you, I'll spend my life in Lebanon."

Sam went in debt some more—quite a bit more—for a fine new wardrobe.

The tailor who outfitted him beamed. "I really ought to give you a special price, Mr. Houston. You're the best walking advertisement a tailor ever had!" He reached up to smooth the coat on Sam's shoulders. "There! Take a look!"

Sam looked in the long mirror. He smiled. "You're quite a tailor!"

"You're a fine figger of a man!"

When Sam rode to The Hermitage late in January, Old Hickory said it, too. "My bellowing young upstart, you're a fine figger of a man!"

Before Sam left, Old Hickory suggested the time for another visit . . . and the next time . . . and the next.

Soon Mrs. Jackson was "Aunt Rachel" to Sam. But Old Hickory—to his face—was always "sir" or "Mr. Jackson."

Sometimes Old Hickory discussed lawsuits with Sam, and they argued for hours—Old Hickory hunched in his chair, grinning over his matched fingertips, Sam striding up and down and booming.

"Shame to waste that parade-ground bellow on one victim," Old Hickory said once. "You ought to be running for office. But I guess you like being in Lebanon, don't you? You *like* being a big frog in a little puddle!"

Sam stared at him, baffled, then angry.

"I've got a bet on you, Sam. Fellow bet me twenty to one you couldn't be elected prosecuting attorney of this district. I got a lot riding on that bet. You going to let me lose that money?"

Sam was glad there was a chair behind him. He sat down.

"Know what that fellow said? He said, 'Why Sam Houston isn't dry behind the ears yet! Run for prosecuting attorney? He's not supposed to be ready for the bar yet! Not for another six months!' Yes, sir, that's what he said. And I just let him go on talking, till he convinced himself he could win that bet. And I made another bet with him, too. That when you did win the election for prosecuting attorney, that Governor McNimm would appoint you adjutant general of the West Tennessee militia, and you'd be Colonel Houston."

"I—I—don't believe I'm following you, sir."

"Very simple. You got nerve to run for office? Or are you going to stick in Lebanon all your life? Be a big frog in a little puddle?"

In October of 1819—less than a year after he came to Lebanon—Sam said good-by. The whole town turned out to see him off.

"Speech, Sam Houston! Speech!"

Sam looked at all the friendly faces and had a hard time swallowing the lump in his throat. "It's an odd thing," he said. "If a road is six miles or sixty east to west, you'd expect it to be six miles or sixty west to east, wouldn't you? When I came to Lebanon, it did not seem far from Nashville. Only thirty miles, west to east. But now that I must leave Lebanon, Nashville seems much farther away."

"You're going farther than Nashville, Sam Houston!" a man yelled. "Lots farther! But we'll always say you belong to us! Because you started your law work here!"

The crowd cheered.

Another yelled, "Farther than that, Sam Houston!"

Farther than that, Sam Houston. . . .

Sam remembered those words four years later as he rode to Washington. Major General Houston now, of the West Tennessee militia, and Congressman Houston from Tennessee.

Washington . . . he thought of the night five years ago when he had sat with his head in his hands and faced the end of his Army career.

A failure at twenty-five. A success at thirty. "Maybe," he said to himself, "it's better to have your hard knocks when you're young. I'd hate to live through that night again."

In 1824 Sam ran for a second term in Congress. Not that he needed to campaign very hard. He did it because he enjoyed it. He was at every barn raising, corn husking, and barbecue in his district, towering head and shoulders over the crowd, laughing, joking, shaking hands.

"Old Hickory's boy," men called him. Sometimes they said "Old Hickory's heir." Old Hickory was running for President of the United States. He'd make it, too, Tennesseeans said. And after Old Hickory . . .

But Old Hickory didn't make it. He got more votes than either of his opponents—Henry Clay and John Quincy Adams—but not a majority of the votes. So the

House of Representatives had to settle the election. They chose John Quincy Adams.

"Just wait till next time!" Old Hickory's backers yelled.

In 1828 Old Hickory won in a landslide.

Now there was more talk that "Old Hickory's boy" would be "Old Hickory's heir." For Sam was governor of Tennessee.

"We've put one man in the White House! We'll put the next one there, too!"

Sam only smiled and said nothing. He did let it be known that he'd run for a second term as governor of Tennessee.

Just now Sam had something else on his mind. He was thinking of Colonel John Allen's big plantation home near Gallatin, in the Cumberland Valley. The Allen home had always reminded Sam of Timber Ridge. A gay, hospitable place, where friends or friends of friends were always welcome. Sam had often stopped there on his way to and from Washington.

Now he was thinking of the Allen home—and a certain pair of blue eyes. Eliza, Colonel Allen's young daughter, had been on his mind for quite a while. But she was so young. Only twenty. Next March he would be thirty-four. What would her family think of him as a husband for Eliza? A man so much older?

The only honorable thing to do, he decided, was to talk to her father before he talked to Eliza. The very first chance . . . And Sam, who could face any crowd anywhere, found his hands sweating and his throat dry when he thought of talking to Colonel Allen. What if Eliza's father laughed at him?

Three times he stopped at the Allen home—and went away without speaking. Once more he went. This time he'd go through with it! Thank heaven, Eliza wasn't there. At a party, her father said.

"Good. I mean—I'd like to talk to you."

"Of course! Come along to the library!"

Sam followed his host. This was worse than leading the charge at Horseshoe Bend.

He knew just what he was going to say. He had practiced it over and over. "Colonel Allen . . ." His mind was blank.

"Yes, Governor Houston?"

His fine speech was gone. He blurted, "I'll be thirty-four in March. But I love Eliza. Before I let her know how I feel I—" He stopped. The thing he had dreaded was happening. Colonel Allen was laughing.

"Sam Houston! How stupid can a bright man be?"

"I see." Sam got up and bowed stiffly. "Thank you, sir, for—"

"Sit down, man! Sit down! Did you think I didn't know how you feel? I've known for a month! Two months!" He held out his hand. "You have my blessing."

"Sir, you've made me the happiest man in the world. If Eliza—"

"Old Hickory's Boy"

"And you'll make me a proud father-in-law!" Colonel Allen said. He did not seem to doubt how Eliza felt. Sam hoped he was right.

The next evening Eliza met Sam at the door. Her look, half smiling, half solemn, told Sam she knew. He had no trouble finding words that night. When he said good night, he and Eliza were engaged.

In January Sam told Old Hickory good-by as he started for Washington. Poor old man! He had aged ten years since Aunt Rachel died.

But Old Hickory could still come up with the unexpected. "Hear I'm going to Washington to keep the chair warm for you, Sam. Good luck, my boy. May your wedded life be as happy as mine was. And—" Old Hickory didn't say more. He only grinned. Men were still wondering whether he'd back Sam Houston or Billy Carroll in the governor's race.

Late in January Sam stood with the minister in the Allen home and watched Eliza on her father's arm coming down the stairs toward him. There was that same expression, half smiling, half solemn, in her eyes.

"If I died this minute," Sam told himself humbly, "I should have had more happiness than most of the world."

There was a night in April when Sam wished he had died that day. He had gone out for a late walk. A young man—hardly more than a boy—was standing in the street, staring at the door as Sam came out. When he saw Sam, the boy wheeled and started away, weaving a little.

91

Someone, Sam decided, had better take care of him. He caught up with the boy. "You wanted to see me? Anything I can do for you?"

"No, you can't do anything for me, Mr. High-and-Mighty." His tongue was thick. He spoke slowly and carefully.

"Here, here!" Sam took hold of his arm. "What have I ever done to you? If I've hurt you, I'm sincerely sorry."

"Hah! You're sorry. Makes everything all right."

"I can't make anything all right till I know what's wrong."

"You took Eliza! That's what! She loved me—*me!* But her family made her marry you. You know why? Because they think you'll be the next President of the United States. That's why!" He jerked loose and lurched away.

Sam did not follow. For a long time he stood motionless. Rage, disbelief, then a gnawing doubt clawed at him. He walked for an hour, trying to get over the shock. It was no use. The only thing to do was to talk to Eliza. She might laugh at him. She might be angry with him for listening to drunken maunderings. Anything was better than not knowing.

He forced himself to speak quietly when he told her about it. "Well, Eliza?"

She turned white and hid her face in her hands. She began to sob.

So it was true! Sam went out into the night again. He

walked until dawn. When he thought he had a grip on himself he returned.

"I'm sorry, Eliza. More sorry than I can ever say. You may get a divorce on the grounds that I have deserted you."

She gasped and stared at him. "But—but—what are you going to do?"

"That won't matter. You'll never see me again."

The Exile

A huge, bearded man slouched on the deck of a river steamer and stared at the water. The other steerage passengers and the deckhands shot sidelong glances at him, but they didn't try to strike up a conversation.

Sam stared at the water, hearing over again the arguments before he had disappeared:

"You can't do this, Sam! Resign as governor, withdraw from the race—without explaining."

"I've done it."

"You've got to explain!"

"This is a painful but private affair. I have nothing to say."

"Sam, if you don't explain, they'll tear your reputation to shreds! They've already burned you in effigy!"

"If my reputation can't stand the strain, let me lose it."

"But, Sam . . ."

Near Sam on the deck of the steamer a little family with three small children huddled among their belongings. The young mother held a baby in her arms. The next child was a toddler, still unsteady on his feet. The oldest little boy might have been five. He was keeping a big-brotherly eye on the toddler. The toddler stumbled, sat up, and blinked, as though deciding whether to laugh or cry.

"Big brother" patted his back. "That's a boy, Willie!"

Sam winced and shut his eyes. It had been that way when he was five and Willie was two. He had "big brothered" Willie, had taught him to take his tumbles without bawling.

"Stop it," he told himself. Stop thinking about it! But he could not keep from watching the two little boys. He had dreamed of having little boys of his own, of teaching them to take their tumbles.

The sunset began to glow. He turned his back on the children and looked down into the water. Tonight he'd do it. Just slip overboard in the darkness. Very quietly. Just slide over the side and go under. Then swim away from the boat until . . . People said a drowning man fought to live. Not always. Not when he had nothing to live for. Tonight . . .

Something caught his eye. A bird rose with a whirr of wings and mounted into the sunset. A black silhouette against the orange sky. A raven? The bird climbed, then wheeled and flew due west into the setting sun.

Sam stood, turned, and watched the bird's flight until

95

it was a speck in the sky. Into the west. . . . Was it a sign?

"My son!" Oo-loo-te-ka said, "You have come home!"

"Yes. The Raven has come home."

"Eleven winters have passed since we said good-by. But my heart has wandered often where you were. We have heard that you were a great chief among your people. Then, when a dark cloud fell on your spirit, you thought of us. You are welcome. My home is yours. My wigwam is yours. Rest with me."

"I don't need rest!" Sam burst out. "Give me work to do! Work!"

Where was he? He had been dreaming of the Battle of Horseshoe Bend. The doctor had been working on his shoulder. Now he wakened and the dream was gone. Only the pain was there. His shoulder was hurting like the very devil. Where was he?

He heard someone speak in the next room. "This is going to hurt, Captain Moore. We've got to set your arm."

Sam recognized the voice. It was young Lieutenant Howard. Now he knew where he was. Last night he had dropped in for a chat with the soldiers stationed at Fort Gibson, not far from Oo-loo-te-ka's village.

He remembered drinking with this visiting officer, Captain Moore. He remembered the captain's one-sided smile and his prying eyes. "Tell me, General Houston, just what was the trouble between you and your wife?"

Then the fight. It must have been quite a fight, Sam decided, if he had broken the captain's arm.

When had he lain down on this bunk?

He lay with his eyes closed, remembering the last two years. August of 1831 now. Almost two and a half years since he had come to Oo-loo-te-ka's village—since he had said, "Give me work to do! Work!"

At first he had kept busy, riding from one Indian village to another, checking on conditions, finding what the crooked Indian agents and traders had been doing to the Indians.

When the government had talked of moving some Indians farther west, he had kept busy with that. He had tried to get a contract to furnish rations for the Indians. He could have done an honest job of it, too. He could have furnished decent rations at half what the government had paid for rations before. But Washington had dropped the plan for the time being.

For almost two years he had kept busy, riding from place to place, writing letters to Washington, writing newspaper articles—anything to keep busy. Busy enough to forget.

It had been a losing fight—working to forget. These last few months he had been drinking to forget—and waking up to remember.

He heard young Mr. Howard say, "There you are,

Captain Moore. Nice, clean break. You won't have any trouble with your arm. Now, let's see what we can do about your face."

The captain's voice was shaking with fury. "Just wait till he sobers up! I'll—"

"I wouldn't do anything, sir." Mr. Howard's voice was quiet. "If you make a scene, it's going to come out why the fight started. That you thought he was so drunk you could pry into his life. You wouldn't want to have men say you were—*nosy*—would you, sir?"

"I'll ruin him! I'll—"

"You can't ruin Sam Houston, sir." Mr Howard's voice was sad. "He's doing that for himself. I remember when he came West the spring of twenty-nine. It's unbelievable what's happened since he just—let go. So, why don't you just forget about Sam Houston, sir? It's the only thing to do."

Someone hammered on the door, then flung it open. There were shouts of "Mail! Yeah! Mail!"

Sam recognized Ben Smithers' voice. "Come and get it, boys!" Presently he said, "And I've got a message for Sam Houston. Someone ought to see that he gets it right off."

" 'Big Drunk' is here," the captain snarled. "You'd better give him a day or two to sleep it off."

Sam struggled to his feet, staggered to the door, and gripped the frame. "What is it?"

Old Ben hurried to his side, looking at him anxiously. "You know me, General Houston?"

"Of course, Ben. What is the message?"

"Your mother—she's mighty poorly. Asking for you. You understand?"

"Yes. Help me to my horse."

The captain, with his battered face and his arm in a sling, got up. He put the width of a table between him and Sam before he spoke. "Just look at him! The great Sam Houston! Tennessee's favorite governor! Old Hickory's heir! Hah! 'Big Drunk'! That's what the Indians call you now!"

Sam did not answer. With Ben's help he walked a crooked path to the door.

Ben helped him mount. "You sure you'll be all right?"

"Sure. He'll get me to my wigwam. Knows the way. Got more sense than I have. I'll pack and start right away."

The journey to Maryville seemed to take forever. It was in the dead of the night when Sam reached his mother's home. A candle flickered in a window. Was he too late?

He opened the door. His sister Mary ran to his arms. "Sam! Thank God you're in time!" She took him to his mother's bed. "Mother! It's Sam!"

Mother did not stir. Shocked, Sam stared down at the gaunt face. He would not have known her.

He knelt by her bed. "Mother? Is the door of your cottage open to me?"

She stirred. Her eyes opened. Suddenly she was

Mother again. "Sam, dear . . ." Even the faint whisper had the loving warmth he remembered. "Always open to you. A brave man. You'll never . . . turn your back . . . on life."

At the funeral the minister spoke of her pioneer spirit, her gallantry, her courage.

Through it all Sam heard her last words: *You'll never turn your back on life.* The first time in all these years she had forgotten. She always said, "You'll never turn your back to save your life." But this last time she had forgotten . . . or had she? Had she said exactly what she meant to say? *You'll never turn your back on life.*

Sam was pale-faced, grim—and sober—when he stopped at Fort Gibson. A letter waited for him. He read it, then stood in a dazed silence. Was this his chance to start over? Some financiers in New York City wanted to talk with him about going to Texas for them.

Slowly Sam rode on to Oo-loo-te-ka's village. "My father, The Raven is going toward the rising sun. He shall go many places. He shall see the Great White Father. He shall tell him of the wickedness of the Indian agents."

"The Great Spirit will go with my son," Oo-loo-te-ka said.

In worn buckskins, Sam set out for the East. He wished he could afford a handsome wardrobe to meet this Mr. Prentiss in New York. But he'd do well to get to

New York, on to Washington, and pay room and board. He went downriver to New Orleans and sailed for New York.

At sunset he looked at the water and remembered the bird flying into the west. Texas . . . was that "the west" of that omen? Only time—and Mr. Prentiss— could answer that.

If Sam's battered appearance startled Mr. Prentiss, he did not show it. He got down to cases with a question. "General Houston, how much do you know of the recent history of Texas?"

"Not much," Sam said. "I know that about 1819 Spain decided she'd have to bring in foreigners to settle Texas. She worked out a typically Spanish arrangement. She would grant huge tracts of land to leaders of colonies—*empresarios,* she called them. The empresarios would be responsible for bringing in dependable settlers.

"It looked like a happy solution for Spain. Foreigners would settle the land, do the work, run the risks, increase the value of the land, and be a buffer between Mexico and the fierce Indian tribes that Spain could not handle.

"It looked like a happy solution for men who were down on their luck, too. They could get land for a song. They could migrate to Spanish Texas, swear allegiance to Spain, and start over again.

"The first empresario to get a contract was Moses

Austin. He died before he got started. His son, Stephen, took over the job. This Stephen Austin—from what I've heard—has been the most successful of the empresarios. He probably owns so much land now you could drop three of our New England states in his domain, and lose them.

"There was one little switch in things when Austin started his colony. Mexico rebelled from Spain and became independent. So the empresarios—and their settlers—swore allegiance to Mexico instead of to Spain."

"Very neatly put," Mr. Prentiss said. "And now?"

"Mexico is trying to rule Texas—but she hasn't quite learned to rule herself yet. I've lost track of how many rulers she's had. It's been 'Hail and farewell' for one after another. The current one—at last reports—is one Señor Bustamante. He's been cracking down on Texas. And the Texans are getting restless."

"Amazing fund of information, General Houston!"

Sam did not admit how hard he had been studying the situation—the hours he had spent asking questions in New Orleans. How desperately he was fighting for a chance for a new life. If only Mr. Prentiss would say, "You're hired!" If only he would give him an advance to cover expenses!

Now Sam only shrugged and smiled. "A man likes to keep abreast of things."

"I'm sorry I don't have more time this morning, General Houston. Can you see me tomorrow at this same time?"

The Exile

"If I can find a cheaper room," Sam thought. He had to save enough money to get to Washington. He had promised Oo-loo-te-ka he would talk to the Great White Father.

Three other mornings Mr. Prentiss said they would talk further—tomorrow. Finally he said, "If our plans shape up as I hope they will, General Houston, we'd like you to go to Texas as our lawyer."

"How soon will you know?"

"Within another week or two I hope. How long will you be in New York?"

Sam hid his disappointment. "I'm leaving immediately for Washington," he said briskly. "I've some business with President Jackson. You may reach me at Brown's Indian Queen Hotel."

"You'll hear from us as soon as possible."

"It can't be too soon for me!" Sam thought. He paid his hotel bill, counted his cash, and set out for Washington.

When he walked into the Indian Queen Hotel Sam heard a buzz of whispers. He smiled grimly. They had plenty to buzz about.

How would Old Hickory greet him? he wondered. In one of his white-hot rages? Or in cold scorn?

"Sam, my boy!" Old Hickory was haggard, but his eyes were as lively as ever. "Good to see you!" No questions. No reproaches. "I'm sorry I'm short of time this morning, Sam. You've come to talk about Indian agents? Let's have it."

Sam did.

Old Hickory was stunned. "I—I can hardly believe it! Those men—I trusted them to deal honorably with the Indians. But—if what you've told me is true—some heads will roll!"

"Then some heads will roll!" Sam got up. "If you have any questions, I'll be at the Indian Queen."

"How long, Sam?"

"A few days, sir." He hoped it would be only a few days.

"Questions or not, I'll see you again, Sam."

Evidently Old Hickory had no questions. Sam was still waiting for word from Mr. Prentiss when he heard that five Indian agents and subagents had been dismissed. That was that. His work in Washington was done. Should he go back to New York, or wait to hear from Mr. Prentiss?

The next morning Sam's name jumped out at him from a column in the *National Intelligencer*, a violently anti-Jackson paper. His name was in part of a speech quoted from Congressman William Stanberry. Mr. Stanberry had raised a question: Had the 'Honorable' Mr. Eaton been forced to resign from the Cabinet because of fraud in connection with his attempt to get a contract for one Sam Houston to supply Indian rations?

Sam started three letters to Mr. Stanberry before he settled down enough to keep the ink from splattering. Had Mr. Stanberry used his name in the House of Representatives? Had he meant to accuse Sam Houston of fraud?

Mr. Stanberry did not answer Sam. "Tell Mr. Houston that I do not recognize his right to question me."

Sam blazed. "Then I'll get an answer out of him, face to face!" And he gripped his heavy hickory cane.

Washington was agog. There were rumors that Congressman Stanberry was carrying a pistol. Some rumors said a brace of pistols!

A few nights later Sam was walking with Senator Buckner and Congressman Blair. A man came from across the street and disappeared into the shadows ahead of them.

Mr. Blair stopped. "Let's go back."

"Why?" Sam asked.

"That's Stanberry!"

"So?" Sam quickened his pace.

Two days later Sam was under arrest, ordered to stand trial in the House of Representatives, accused of waylaying a member of that august body and doing great bodily harm.

"Our Kind of Country"

Sam's friends rallied round. At the opening of the trial Senator Buckner testified that General Houston had not "waylaid" Congressman Stanberry. He had met up with him accidentally. Senator Buckner heard General Houston say, "Are you William Stanberry?"

Then the ruckus had started. It was too dark for the senator to see much of what happened. He heard the thwacks of the cane. He heard a snap, as though a pistol had misfired, and saw a flash of sparks. Then General Houston had picked up Mr. Stanberry and sent him reeling down the street with a kick. But he had *not* "waylaid" him!

Congressman James K. Polk protested the whole business. This trial was illegal! The House had no right to arrest and try a private citizen!

How did General Houston plead? Guilty or not guilty?

General Houston agreed with Congressman Polk. The trial was not legal.

The House took a vote. The trial went on. Francis Scott Key offered to defend Sam.

"Our Kind of Country"

"He means well," Old Hickory said, "but you'd do better to conduct your own defense."

Sam only shrugged. Day after day he sat through the trial and heard his reputation—if he had any left—being torn to shreds.

Time and again Mr. Key protested. General Houston's unhappy marriage was not on trial! General Houston's years of exile were not on trial! Time and again words were stricken from the record—but Sam knew they were still written in people's minds.

At last the prosecution was through. Mr. Key began the defense. After one day, Old Hickory sent for Sam.

"Key's going to lose this case! You've got to conduct your own defense! Here!" He handed Sam some gold pieces. "Get yourself some decent clothes. Ask for twenty-four hours to prepare your defense—and tell the tailor to hurry!"

"What have clothes to do with it?" Sam asked.

"You want to be sentenced to six months in jail? Or a year?"

Jail! Sam took the money.

He asked for twenty-four hours to "prepare his defense." The House gave him forty-eight hours. The tailor had time to make the suit. Washington had time to hear the news: General Houston would conduct his own defense!

Sam stopped at the White House on his way to the trial.

"That's better!" Old Hickory said. "Sam Houston, gentleman! Ex-governor of the sovereign state of Tennessee! Now, get in there and win that case!"

The prosecution had been savage in its attack. Sam was quietly courteous. He was leisurely. Very leisurely. At last the House told him he would have to close his defense the next day.

When the last morning came the House was filled, there were chairs in the aisles, and the galleries were jammed.

Sam addressed the Speaker, but his voice carried to the last row of the gallery. He had been accused, for the first time in his life, he said, of breaking a law of his country. He had been accused of a dastardly crime—of waylaying a man with intent to kill. He had been branded an assassin. Why? Because he had chastised a man who had branded him before the world as a fraudulent rascal.

The galleries broke out in a storm of applause. Sam waited for silence. A bouquet of roses fell at his feet. Sam picked them up. He bowed.

From the gallery came a woman's voice—high, cool, and clear. "I had rather be Sam Houston in a dungeon than Stanberry on a throne!"

Speaker Stevenson had to pound his gavel for order.

Sam went on. "Though the ploughshare of ruin has been driven over me and laid waste my brightest hopes, I can only say with the poet Byron:

"Our Kind of Country"

I seek no sympathies, nor need.
The thorns that I have reaped are of the tree
I planted; they have torn me and I bleed."

Once more the Speaker had to pound for order.

Then Sam began to hammer on the illegality of the trial. Did a member of the House have the privilege of branding a private citizen a scoundrel? And when legislators lied, did privilege protect them from punishment?

When he finished, even members of the House applauded. But . . . they had to find him guilty. After all, he *had* beaten up Congressman Stanberry. They voted; they found him guilty. They passed sentence. General Houston was to be reprimanded by the Speaker of the House.

Sam walked down the aisle to receive his reprimand.

"I have a duty to perform," Speaker Stevenson said, "but I cannot do it without alluding to the character of the accused. . . . We all know, every one of us, of the high achievements of General Houston. . . . As a soldier he served his nation with intrepid heroism and poured forth blood like water for his nation and his flag. . . . As a citizen he has held numerous high offices of trust. . . . Never has he betrayed that trust or performed his duty without distinction and great honor.

"I forebear to say more, General Houston, than to pronounce the judgment of this House. And that is that you be reprimanded by the Speaker, and I do reprimand you accordingly."

Sam bowed. The Speaker bowed. The gallery gave Sam a standing ovation. If he had just been decorated with three medals, the applause could not have been louder. The Speaker did not pound for silence. He let the applause go on . . . and on.

At the White House, Old Hickory beamed. "What now, Sam?"

Sam told him of the possibility that he'd go to Texas.

"I'd like to have you there," Old Hickory said. "I'd like to see it through your eyes. How soon will you be going?"

Sam thought of the state of his pocketbook. "The sooner the better!"

But Congressman Stanberry was not through with Sam. During the trial he had protested that he had not meant to accuse Sam of fraud, but now he demanded that a committee investigate the charge of fraud in the Indian rations affair. The committee sat. It investigated. It brought witnesses from beyond the Mississippi. The result—no evidence of fraud.

Mr. Stanberry tried again. He went to the Federal Court, accusing Sam of criminal assault. That trial dragged on into June. In spite of the muggy heat, Sam felt a cold chill settle under his ribs. This trial was going against him. He was going to be found guilty. What would the sentence be? Six months in jail? Or a year? Or longer? He'd rather be dead!

"Our Kind of Country"

The court passed sentence. General Houston was found guilty. He was fined $500, but given a year to pay the fine. A good thing, Sam thought. He could not have paid a fine of five dollars—unless he borrowed the money. If only he would hear from New York! He did. A cholera epidemic was raging. Business was at a standstill. Maybe later . . .

Sam made up his mind. He was going to have a look at Texas if he had to borrow money to get there!

Old Hickory gave Sam a commission to carry out for the United States in Texas. Sam was to see the Comanche Indians, who roamed from Texas into the western part of the Louisiana Purchase. The United States was talking of moving some Indian tribes farther west. But more peaceful tribes would be wary of settling where the fierce Comanches sometimes roamed.

Late in 1832 Sam rode into Texas. What was ahead for him? A new life? He would be thirty-nine next March. Could a man start over that late? A man who had failed as miserably as he had?

He rode toward the little town of Nacogdoches in eastern Texas. A beautiful location, he thought, between two rivers. But not much of a town. The walls of a Spanish fort remained from another day. Most of the other buildings were log cabins, some shingled over. They reminded him of early Knoxville. A pioneer world. Could it be a place to begin again? "A stranger in a strange land," he thought as he rode into the town.

Someone yelled, "Sam Houston!" Two men came running. Both were from Tennessee.

Soon he was in Brown's Tavern with three dozen men, all talking at once.

Presently one man shouted, "All right! Let's get to the point! You said you wanted a leader who could lick those damned Mexicans! Now you've—"

A quiet man got to his feet slowly. "*Those* Mexicans, sir? *Those* Mexicans? Aren't *we* citizens of Mexico? Didn't we come to this new land to start over? Didn't we swear allegiance to the government that gave us this chance?"

The first man turned red, then yelled, "I swore allegiance to the Republic of Mexico! To a country that was supposed to be ruled by the Constitution of 1824! But Mexico under Bustamante is no republic! Bustamante is a tyrant and you know it!"

Most of the crowd cheered. Arguments began. Nacogdoches seemed to be divided into firebrands and coolheads—and the firebrands were leading, about twenty to one. They were ready to fight. The coolheads wanted peace. Yes, they were having trouble with Bustamante, but surely they could settle things without fighting. Just look how long Stephen Austin had—

The mention of Austin's name brought yells from the firebrands. Texas couldn't depend on Stephen Austin! He thought like a Mexican!

The quiet man got up again. "Not depend on Austin?

"Our Kind of Country"

I'd say he's the hope of Texas. A lot of men have had contracts to be empresarios. Most of them have failed. Why? Because they didn't have what it takes. Austin has the patience of Job and the courage of a lion!"

Some of the coolheads nodded. But the firebrands argued. No one was going to get justice now without fighting for it. They aired their main grievances:

Texas was not a separate state; it was combined with Coahuila, the province just south of the Rio Grande, into the state of Coahuila-Texas. Coahuila had more people than Texas. She packed the legislature. The only laws passed were those that favored Coahuila. When and if Texas had a population of 80,000, she could ask to be a separate state.

But now there was no chance that she'd ever have that many people. Bustamante had cut off immigration. He was strangling Texas in every way he could. He had ended the days of duty-free imports of household goods and tools. Now duties were so high that Texans could not pay them.

"What's the good of petitions?" someone yelled.

Texas had held a convention last October and sent a petition to Bustamante. What had happened? Stern commands! It was illegal to call a convention! If they did it again, they would suffer the penalty!

"I say we've got to fight!"

The argument began again.

Someone yelled, "Let Sam Houston talk!"

"I've nothing to say," Sam told them. "I did not come to Texas to start a rebellion. I have a mission from President Jackson to treat with the Comanche Indians."

Silence. Men studied him with narrowed eyes. He could feel their questions: Is he telling the truth? Who'll he side with? The War Party? Or the Peace Party?

After a few days Sam said good-by to the firebrands of Nacogdoches. He must ride west. Yes, he promised, he'd see them again on his return.

Before he went on west to San Antonio, he'd make one stop. This Stephen Austin was the man he wanted to see. He took the ferry across the Brazos River. What a beautiful river it was—wide and deep. And what beautiful country. He drew a deep breath. It didn't take a man long to fall in love with Texas.

He rode into the little town of San Felipe de Austin, which was the capital of Austin's colony. He stopped at the Virginia House.

"Mr. Austin?" The innkeeper shook his head. Mr. Austin was out somewhere in his colony. No telling where, or when he'd be back. Man could ride two weeks and never see the half of it.

Someone yelled, "Sam Houston!"

Sam turned. A big man with reddish hair and smiling gray eyes was coming toward him. He was dressed in the height of Spanish fashion, but he still had the famous knife at his belt.

"Jim Bowie!"

Sam had met Jim once, and no man who had ever met

"Our Kind of Country"

Jim Bowie was going to forget him. The most famous fighter in the whole Southwest! Once he had stood off three bandits with his bowie knife.

"You've come to the right place, Sam," Jim said. "Texas is our kind of country. Where you heading for?"

"San Antonio de Bexar. Then—"

Jim smiled when Sam pronounced "Bexar" the way it looked. "The Spanish pronounce *x* like our *h*," he said. "Just call it "Bare" and you'll be as close as most Anglo-Americans ever get to pronouncing it."

"You can talk Spanish?"

"And French. After all, I grew up in Louisiana. Heard them more than English."

"You're lucky!"

"You don't know *how* lucky!" There was a gentleness in Jim's voice. He told of his happy marriage to Ursula Veramendi, the young daughter of the vice-governor of Coahuila-Texas. They had two children—first a little girl, then a son. Jim grinned. "Was I proud when *he* was born! A man likes to have—" He stopped.

The old ache of loneliness hit Sam. Almost four years —but time didn't help much. He forced himself to smile. "You think Jim-the-Second will be as famous a fighter as his father?"

"I've settled down, Sam. There's nothing like a happy marriage—" Jim stopped again.

"I remember," Sam said, "you always claimed you never *started* a fight. You just finished them."

Jim laughed. "I'll ride with you to Bexar." He'd stop

there to see his father-in-law, Señor Veramendi. Delightful man. Sam would like him. Then Jim would ride south to his home in the mountains. Why didn't Sam come along?

"Some other time," Sam promised. "I must finish this mission for President Jackson first." He was glad of the excuse. A happy home with little children . . . not yet.

They rode west together. Everywhere people smiled at Jim and let their smiles spill over on Sam, too. Any friend of Jim Bowie's seemed to be a friend of half of Texas.

As they neared San Antonio Jim said, "Might as well take our time. Won't be anybody stirring for the next three hours."

"Why not?"

"Siesta. No Latin-American does anything but rest this time of day. Let's stop at the Alamo. Interesting place. Ruins of an old mission."

Stone walls, four feet thick, enclosed what was left of the chapel. Other walls, not so thick, enclosed two or three acres of land beyond it.

"Built as a mission," Jim said, "then used as a fort."

Sam looked around. "Not much of a fort. Those walls might stop Indian arrows, but they couldn't stand against our cannons today. Not thick enough. Not high enough, either. An enemy could scale them just like that."

"What would the men inside be doing when the enemy was trying to scale the walls?"

"They'd be getting their heads shot off. No portholes. A man would have to expose head and shoulders to take aim."

"So you don't think it's much of a fort?" Jim asked.

"It's a death trap."

When siesta time was over they rode into town. Odd-looking place, the Veramendi home, Sam thought. Nothing but bare walls, flush with the street. No grounds, no flowers, no trees, no . . . They went inside and he saw another world. The trees and flowers were in a huge central court, with all the rooms of the house opening on it. The heavy walls shut out the heat, the noise, the dust—the whole world. These Latin-Americans knew how to build!

They knew how to make a man feel at home, too. Señor Veramendi said, "Señor, my home is yours!" and made it sound as though he meant it.

In this stately home, too, any friend of Jim Bowie's seemed welcome. Sam basked in the friendliness.

Señor Veramendi lifted his eyebrows when he heard that Sam was to talk with the Comanches. "They are very fierce, señor."

"If any man can talk with them," Jim declared, "Sam Houston can. He can *think* like an Indian."

"They are very fierce," Señor Veramendi repeated. When Sam said good-by and set out to find the Comanches, Señor Veramendi said, "*Vaya con Dios,* señor. Go with God."

Comanches were reported northwest of San Antonio.

"But I'd not go into their country without a regiment!" a man said.

Sam rode on alone. The third day he was suddenly surrounded by a dozen painted horsemen, with arrows ready to loose.

He raised his hand in a sign of peace.

Slowly they lowered their bows. Still wary and alert, they took him to their village. The head chief was away, but Sam talked in sign language to their other leaders. He gave them medals with President Jackson's portrait for their chiefs. When he left them, he had their promise they would send word to all their people. They would try to meet with the Indian agent of the Great White Father.

Sam started east again, smiling. Jim Bowie was right. Texas was his kind of country. How vast it was! How untamed! A man could spend his life building something here!

All the people had made him feel welcome—from the firebrands of Nacogdoches to the gracious Señor Veramendi. Even the Comanches. Yes, Texas was his land. It would be his home.

He'd write Old Hickory "mission accomplished." Then he'd settle down in Nacogdoches. If Mr. Prentiss-and-company ever got around to hiring him as their lawyer, he'd be conveniently on the spot. Meantime he could make his way on his own.

But first he wanted to see Stephen Austin.

"Our Kind of Country"

He stopped again in San Felipe de Austin. That man with "the patience of Job and the courage of a lion"—what sort of man would he be? A smiling giant like Jim Bowie, equally at home with the roughest frontiersman and the most polished gentleman? He knocked on Austin's door.

"Come!"

Smiling, Sam entered—and felt the smile growing stiff on his face. He was glad of his Indian training. He knew he did not show his surprise. Was this Stephen Austin—this small, slim man with the face of a tired scholar? He looked more like a professor than a pioneer. "Mr. Austin, I'm Sam Houston."

"I know." Austin's voice was cool, almost cold. "I heard you were in Texas. I've heard rumors about you, Mr. Houston. I hope they are not true. If the rumors about you are true, you are not welcome here."

The General
vs. the Council

If the rumors about you are true . . .

So that was how Austin felt. Sam counted to ten, then spoke quietly. "Rumors about me? And what are they?"

"That you're here to stir up trouble and start a rebellion."

Sam smiled. "I didn't know anybody needed to 'stir up trouble.' I thought you were already having trouble."

Austin's eyes grew colder. "Mr. Houston, I've been here ten years. I've seen lots of trouble. But I haven't had to go to war to settle it! Do you know anything about the beginning of my colony?"

"I know your father had the first empresario contract with Spain. That he died and you took over. That, just about that time, Mexico rebelled against Spain, so the contracts continued under Mexican rule."

Austin's smile was wry. "Just like that. Sounds simple, doesn't it? When I started, I borrowed money to buy a little vessel to carry supplies. She was lost on the second voyage. Everything was lost. Settlers were pouring in. I needed to be two dozen places at the same time.

"Then came that little matter you summed up so neatly—that the empresario contracts continued under Mexican rule. I found I would have to go to Mexico City to iron that out. A month's hard riding there, a month's hard riding back. Even if I could settle the questions overnight, I'd have to leave my colony at that critical time for two months. Do you know how long I had to stay in Mexico City, Mr. Houston? A year. Can you imagine the state of my colony when I got back?"

Sam didn't try to answer.

"Yes, Mr. Houston, I've had trouble. But I've lived through it. I've made a peaceful and prosperous colony out of that hard beginning. My people like the world they've found in Texas. In the United States most of them would be tenant farmers, sweating their lives out for a landowner. Here they are landowners themselves. They like it this way. And I'm going to keep it this way! And I'll do it without war!"

"In spite of Bustamante?" Sam asked.

"I've seen quite a few rulers come and go, Mr. Houston. Bustamante won't last forever."

Austin, Sam decided, knew what he was talking about. Not long after, another leader rose against Bustamante. General Santa Anna cried, "Down with tyrants!

Long live the Constitution of 1824! Long live the Republic of Mexico!"

The people cheered. They elected Santa Anna president, to take office in April of 1833.

Texans cheered. They rose against the soldiers of Bustamante and threw them out of Texas. They called a convention. They would draw up another petition and send it to Santa Anna! This time they would get somewhere!

Nacogdoches elected Sam to be one of their delegates to the convention. Some old-time Texans lifted their eyebrows at that. Wasn't he rather new to be sitting in the convention?

David Burnet had things to say. He was a short, chunky lawyer with a row of whiskers under his chin, such as sea captains wore. He had had an empresario contract but had not made a success of it. Evidently he did not have what Austin had. The courage of a lion, perhaps, but not the patience of Job. An odd, stiff, grim, unbending man. Rumor said he carried a pistol in one pocket and a Bible in the other. He neither drank nor swore. A man with Sam Houston's reputation, Burnet said, was no fit representative for the convention. Other men laughed.

"Come on, Burnet! We accept a man for what he *is*, not what he was."

Burnet's eyes froze.

But Sam was a delegate to the convention. The delegates swore allegiance to Santa Anna and the Constitution of 1824. They drew up a petition asking Santa Anna to cancel Bustamante's harsh rulings: to lift the ban against immigration, to remove the heavy import duties, and—above all—to let Texas be a separate state.

They asked Austin to take their petition to Mexico City. War Party and Peace Party agreed on that. He was the man to do it. How long would it take him? How soon could he be back?

"Gentlemen!" he pleaded. "I do not know how long it will take. If you think someone else can work more quickly, send him."

No, no! Austin was the man! The impatient Texans promised to wait—and to stir up no trouble while they waited.

Months passed. The only news from Austin was that there was no news yet. Santa Anna was vacationing at his country estate. The vice-president was in charge. Cholera was raging. Things were very unsettled.

Cholera struck closer home than Mexico City. Jim Bowie lost his wife and both little children. He was a broken man. He was drinking heavily. Some men feared him. David Burnet scorned him. Sam wished he could think of something to say that would help. He hoped something bigger than grief would help Jim pull himself together and go on. He was too fine a man to be lost.

More months passed. Texans began to mutter. Why had they sent Austin, anyhow? What was he doing?

Why didn't he . . . Then news came that shocked the whole countryside. Austin had been arrested and thrown in a dungeon!

Impossible! There must be some mistake! Bustamante was not in power now! This was Santa Anna! The man who had cried, "Down with tyrants! Long live the Constitution of 1824!" Santa Anna wouldn't do a thing like that!

Refugees began fleeing across the Rio Grande into Texas. One of the most honored Mexicans, Lorenzo de Zavala, fled to Texas with a price on his head. Texans knew Zavala and liked him. The son of his first marriage was a fine young man, they said. And after his first wife's death, Zavala had married a girl from the United States. He had been a firm supporter of Santa Anna— and now he had fled with a price on his head. Because he had defied Santa Anna.

Sam went with two friends from Nacogdoches to Zavala's ranch on Buffalo Bayou. He wanted to see the man who had defied Santa Anna.

Zavala, at first sight, was more of a surprise than Austin. Small and chubby, he looked more like a dancing master than a fiery rebel. But when he spoke, there was no doubt about the fire.

"We are all in this together, my friends! North and south of the Rio Grande! Santa Anna is a madman!"

Zavala's son, Lorenzo, Jr., was taller than his father, picture-book handsome, and dressed in the height of fashion. But one felt the steel beneath his ruffles. "Santa Anna has not yet honored me with a price on my head, but the day will come! Texas will rise against him, and I shall fight with Texas!"

They went in the ranch house to meet Zavala's young wife and his "second family." The smallest boy rolled big brown eyes at Sam, studied him long and hard, and reached up his arms. Sam picked him up.

Señora Zavala had a charming smile. "You have a way with children, Mr. Houston!"

Sam did not try to answer. He was afraid his voice would shake.

One of the Texans tried to express his sympathy over the tragedy that had struck her home—losing their estates in Mexico, having to flee for their lives.

"Trouble," she said. "But not tragedy. God has been good to us. We are together." She smiled down at the children. "Come, darlings. We'll leave the men to talk of solemn things."

Zavala painted a grim picture. Santa Anna was wiping out every sign of a republic—deposing governors, dismissing legislatures. Putting every state under military rule.

So far only one state, Zacatecas, had tried to protest. Santa Anna's soldiers had swarmed in, burning and killing. Over two thousand men, women, and children had been butchered. That, Santa Anna said, would be the fate of any state that defied him.

Three troubled men rode back to Nacogdoches. What could they do? Without endangering the life of Austin?

Weeks dragged into months. The arguments between War Party and Peace Party grew more bitter. Then, in September of 1835, express riders raced through Texas with the news: Stephen Austin is back!

People flocked to Brazoria where he landed. They stared at him in shocked silence—a ghost of a man with a racking cough.

What would he have to say?

He stood before the gathering with heartsick eyes. "It is no use," he said. "No man can reason with Santa Anna. The only answer is war."

People gasped, then shouted and stamped. War Party and Peace Party were together.

Austin motioned for silence. "We must keep our heads," he said. "We must call a convention— No, we'd better say 'consultation'; a convention is illegal. We shall call a consultation. Let every county send its ablest men."

Nacogdoches did not wait for the consultation. They called a mass meeting of their district, elected Sam commander in chief of the army of the District of Nacogdoches, and authorized him to raise an army.

Sam sent express riders with a call-to-arms through the district. He sent another call-to-arms to New Orleans, to his long-time friend, William Christy. The "redlanders" of eastern Texas came flocking in. Sam began drilling them.

The General vs. the Council

Word came from William Christy. A committee had raised funds to outfit two companies of infantry. The New Orleans Grays would soon be on their way. And Mr. Christy had sent the call-to-arms to other states, too. Sam would be hearing from them!

Western Texas was not waiting for the consultation, either. Volunteers gathered by tens, twenties, and fifties. They elected Austin their commander.

He tried to protest. He was no military man. But the volunteers shouted him down. He was the only man they'd all follow! So Austin, though he was almost too sick to sit in the saddle, rode off to their camp to try to get some order out of chaos.

Soon riders dashed through the country with fresh news. The Mexicans were coming toward San Antonio! Before the consultation met, Texans had already clashed with the Mexicans. They routed them from the little town of Gonzales. The Texans swaggered. That for the Mexicans! This war wouldn't last long!

At last the consultation met—or tried to meet. Half of the delegates were with the army. More delay until they could be brought back.

Hot arguments began. Should they declare their independence? Or should they only say "Down with tyrants! Long live the Constitution of 1824"?

Zavala urged that Texans should not declare their independence. If Texas offered to stand by the Constitution of 1824 and fought bravely, some states south of the Rio Grande might take heart and join her. Sam sided with Zavala. After a long, hot argument they carried the point.

Now they must write a state constitution, elect a temporary governor. . . . The delegates were getting impatient. More Mexicans were in Texas. General Cos, with twelve hundred men, was at San Antonio!

The delegates slapped together a constitution and decided they'd have another meeting, March 1, at Washington-on-the-Brazos—a little farther inland. Maybe it would be safer than San Felipe. They also elected a temporary governor—Henry Smith, a peppery little man of the War Party, and a General Council of thirteen to assist him. They elected Sam Houston commander in chief of the regular army—when he raised it—but gave the General Council the right to appoint officers. A crazy arrangement, Sam thought, but he hoped for the best. Maybe—just maybe—the General Council would see things his way.

The consultation sent Austin and two other men to the United States to try to raise money. Austin's volunteer army elected Colonel Burleson, an experienced Indian fighter, to succeed him. Nobody questioned that. Volunteers *always* elected their own leaders. General Houston was to raise the *regular* army.

At his headquarters in San Felipe Sam made his plans. He sent names to the General Council, asking those men to be appointed to help him. He asked them to vote money to raise his army. No answer from the Council. They were busy arguing with Governor Smith.

The General vs. the Council

At San Antonio the reckless, impatient volunteers decided they were tired of laying siege to San Antonio. They'd take the town. Utterly impossible . . . but they did it. General Cos and twelve hundred men surrendered. What in the name of heaven could the Texans do with twelve hundred prisoners? They paroled General Cos and his men, on their pledge that they would never take up arms against Texas again. They sent an escort to see the army across the Rio Grande. Hurrah! The war was over!

In San Felipe Sam tried to talk to the Council. "The war has just begun! Santa Anna will come. He'll wait till the rise of grass. But by late February—the first of March at the very latest—he'll be here. We've got to be ready to withstand a huge army before the first of March!"

The Council appointed half a dozen officers. They did nothing else. Sam wrote an urgent letter. Maybe that would get an answer.

It did. The Council ordered him to transfer his headquarters forty miles upriver to the little mud-and-shanty town of Washington-on-the-Brazos.

Governor Smith's famous temper blazed. "Those scoundrels! We ought to bring in the army, throw out the Council, and—"

"No," Sam told him. "That's what we're fighting against—military leaders who destroy the civilian government."

"But what's going to become of us?"

"I don't know. I'm using the half dozen men the Council did give me. Stationing them where they can receive the men coming in from the United States. Maybe they'll whip them into shape."

He rode north to the mud-and-shanty town that was Washington-on-the-Brazos. One long building had been put up for meetings. No doors or windows yet. No shutters. Sam knocked together a table and bench and set up headquarters in one end of the place.

Since his hands were tied about recruiting an army, he spent the time writing letters. To friends in the United States, asking their help for Austin and the committee. To the most dependable men of Texas, talking to them of the next convention.

One day someone spoke from the door. "So here's where you are." It was George Hockley, a long-time friend, who had answered Sam's first call-to-arms and come to Nacogdoches.

The army at San Antonio was melting away, Hockley said. Coming and going. No discipline. "I decided to join you. Had trouble finding you, sir."

"I think that was the idea in sending me here," Sam said.

An express brought a letter from Governor Smith. He'd heard rumors the Mexicans were trying to stir up the Cherokee Indians in northeastern Texas to get into the fight against Texas.

Hockley whistled. "Any danger of that?"

"Plenty," Sam said. "Those Cherokees have no reason to love Texas."

Landowners of Nacogdoches were repeating the pattern he'd seen in the United States—trying to drive the Indians off their land.

"I've said my say about it in Nacogdoches," Sam finished. "I didn't please some of the people with my remarks. Well, I'll have to go talk to The Bowl and his young braves. . . ."

A mud-spattered express dashed in with a letter. "From Colonel Neill at the Alamo, sir! It's urgent!"

Sam scanned the letter, stared, unbelieving, then read it again. "But that's impossible!"

"I know, sir," the express said. "But it's happened!"

Sow the Wind . . .

"What's wrong?" Hockley asked.

Sam let him read the letter for himself. Colonel Johnson and a Dr. Grant had decided to invade Mexico. First they would capture the city of Matamoros. They had taken all the able-bodied men from the Alamo, leaving only the sick and wounded. Moreover, they had stripped the Alamo of supplies—arms, ammunition, food, blankets—even medicine.

And who had given permission for them to invade Mexico? The General Council.

"Two thousand men," Sam said, "could stand off an invasion of Texas. But it would take five thousand men—trained and equipped—to invade Mexico! The whole idea is mad!"

He wrote orders for Colonel Fannin, who was south at Refugio, organizing the troops coming in from the United States. Fannin was hard to work with—overbearing and stubborn—but at least he had had two years at West Point. He'd see the idiocy of this expedition. Sam wrote that he would be in Refugio as soon as possible. Meantime Colonel Fannin would take steps to break up that expedition to Matamoros.

He handed the orders to one express. "By day and night to Refugio!"

He wrote a second letter to Governor Smith. The matter of the Cherokees would have to wait. The governor would please send immediate permission for General Houston to go south instead. He enclosed Colonel Neill's letter from the Alamo and wrote, "Send supplies to the wounded, the sick, the naked, and the hungry, for God's sake!" He gave that letter to the other express. "To San Felipe as fast as you can make it! I've got to have an answer in thirty hours!"

It was night when the express brought Governor Smith's permission for Sam to go south. He and Hockley did not wait for dawn to start.

Six days' hard riding brought them to Goliad, a town twenty-odd miles from Refugio. It was night when they arrived. Major Morris was there with the New Orleans Grays. He was marching the next day, he said, to join Dr. Grant at Refugio.

"You will parade your men at six in the morning," Sam told him. "I have something to say."

"Yes, sir. That's all, sir? . . . Then good night."

"All for tonight," Sam thought. "But in the morning . . ." So Dr. Grant was at Refugio. Colonel Fannin would be taking care of *him!*

The next morning Sam saw something he had not noticed in the dark the night before. A notice posted on the wall of the fort. He saw the flourish of Colonel Fannin's signature across the bottom of the notice and smiled. Good man! He was already stopping that Matamoros expedition! Sam began to read. The notice called for all volunteers to march under Colonel Fannin to Matamoros. It ended with a promise: *The men would be paid out of the first spoils.*

Impossible! No man trained at West Point would invite soldiers to engage in piracy! But . . . there it was.

The soldiers assembled. Standing on the gray wall of the fort at Goliad, Sam addressed them. They did not have either the men or the equipment to invade enemy country, he told them. As for the promise that they would be paid out of the spoils—that turned the expedition into piracy. What would the rest of the world think of Texas?

Major Morris listened, at first frowning impatiently, then looking thoughtful.

Sam was still talking when an express came from the Alamo. Colonel Neill asked to be relieved to go to the aid of his sick family. Sam scrawled a note on the message and said, "To Governor Smith at San Felipe!"

He turned back to the men. Point by point he hammered home his arguments. The distance—the lack of provisions on the way—the impossibility of a small force holding Matamoros if they ever did take it, which they couldn't. They'd never even reach there. He was getting through to them. He could feel it in the air.

Sow the Wind . . .

Jim Bowie—Colonel Bowie he was now—dashed up. Scouts had reported a Mexican army marching toward the Alamo. The fort needed immediate reinforcements!

Sam wrote orders for Colonel Neill. He would get his furlough. An officer would be sent to relieve him. Meantime he was to remove the sick and wounded, fetch away the guns, and blow up the Alamo! That was no place to make a stand.

He sent Jim to the Alamo with some volunteers to help with the removal. He sent another express to Governor Smith with the latest news. "What next?" he wondered. He turned back to Major Morris.

Major Morris was deep in thought. "You may be right, sir, but my orders are to join Dr. Grant."

Sam didn't argue. "Very well. I'm on my way to Refugio, too. I'll go along with you." The men would be thinking all the way as they marched. By the time they got to Refugio . . .

Neither Colonel Johnson nor Colonel Fannin was in Refugio when they arrived. Dr. Grant was there with his men, all on their toes and eager to start.

Sam ordered the men paraded and began to talk. He had not said ten sentences when Colonel Johnson dashed up.

Without a "By your leave, sir"—without even a "sir" —Colonel Johnson interrupted. "Orders for you, Houston!"

Sam opened the letter. The General Council had appointed Colonel Johnson and Colonel Fannin to command over all volunteers—which meant all the men. General Houston was relieved of that duty. He would go north immediately, as directed, to treat with the Cherokee Indians.

Colonel Johnson stuck his thumbs in his belt. He spoke so the last man could hear. "So, Houston, you're relieved of command. Going to argue about it?"

Sam's voice carried too. "I should not think of arguing about it. This is a republic, not a military dictatorship. I only regret that the General Council—untrained in military maneuvers—will send hundreds of brave young men to certain defeat and death. Good day, gentlemen, and God pity you."

He rode away. He could only hope he had planted enough doubts in enough minds.

Hockley and two other men joined him. "But, sir—" Hockley began.

"I'm starting north immediately. You coming with me? . . . Good. We'd better eat before we set out."

"But, sir, a few more words from you and the men would have pitched Johnson out. They would have—"

"No, Hockley! If I don't like the way the government is running things, I can resign. But I won't lead a rebellion against it."

"But, sir, for the sake of the country—"

"That's all, Hockley."

While they were eating, a group of citizens of Refugio came to talk to Sam. "General Houston, we've elected you to be our delegate at the March convention in Washington-on-the-Brazos."

Sam smiled. "Thank you, gentlemen, but I don't think I can represent two settlements. And Nacogdoches—"

"Uh—sir—that's why we've elected you. Nacogdoches . . . seems like some of them didn't like what you said about land-grabbers taking land from the Cherokee Indians."

"I see." Sam got up. He could not eat more. If he had tried, the food would have stuck in his throat. "Thank you, gentlemen. I'll be glad to be your delegate to the convention."

He started north again. The whole desperate ride to Refugio had been for nothing. All his work had been for nothing. Removed by the General Council. Rejected by Nacogdoches.

Now another ride, longer and harder, into the Cherokee country. "For two cents," he thought, "I'd just keep going! I'd ride clear out of Texas! I'd let Texas—"

You'll never turn your back. . . .

Why did he have to remember those words now? He rode on in silence. No one tried to talk to him. The next day they didn't talk, either.

Toward evening Sam straightened in his saddle. "I've some hard riding to do if I talk to the Cherokees and get back to Washington-on-the-Brazos in time for the convention."

He heard Hockley's sigh of relief.

In Cherokee country The Bowl, chief of the village, smiled at Sam. But the eyes of the young braves smoldered. Sam did not blame them. He strolled through the village, talking to the people. He sat by the campfire. He listened.

After two days Hockley was worried. "Sir, you haven't much time!"

"That's right," Sam agreed. "And I haven't even started talking about the treaty, have I? Just wasting time. Maybe—just maybe—that's why I was sent to deal with the Cherokees instead of you."

"I'm sorry, sir."

"That's all right. We all have to learn the ways of other people." And he told Hockley of his time in San Antonio and the siesta. "Every time I said 'Let's go now,' Jim Bowie was always saying 'Siesta time. No Latin-American will do anything but rest for the next three hours.' I had to learn."

"Thank you, sir. But I hope it won't be too much longer. You'll be needed at that convention!"

Even after things calmed down, Sam had to talk long and earnestly before The Bowl's Indians agreed to a peace treaty with Texans. Sam promised the Texans would honor the land grant the Cherokees had from the Spanish—that they would give other land in place of land that had been taken.

"I sign for my people," Sam explained. "I take a copy

of the treaty back. I tell them that you have promised not to make war on us. I tell them they must make a promise to you. They must agree to honor this treaty."

"The word of The Raven is enough for my people," The Bowl said. "He walks a straight path. He does not speak with a split tongue."

"The Raven is not the chief of his people. He must talk to the head men," Sam told him.

"The word of The Raven is enough" was all The Bowl said.

They left The Bowl's village with time—just time—to reach Washington-on-the-Brazos by March 1. High water marooned them one whole day and night. Then Hockley's horse pulled up lame.

"Follow as soon as you can!" Sam ordered. He rode on alone.

It was dusk the night of February 29 when he crossed the Brazos and climbed the slope toward the town. To-morrow the convention would begin. March 2 would be his birthday—his forty-third. What did he have to show for forty-three years? "You're quite a success," he thought. Kicked out of his command of the army. Re-jected by Nacogdoches. If Refugio hadn't elected him, he'd not even be a delegate to the convention.

His horse plodded along the muddy, stump-dotted road that was the "main street." Sam saw several tents, and men huddled around campfires. Not enough houses —even shacks—to take care of the delegates. The "town hall" still lacked doors and windows. Someone had tacked cloth over the windows to try to keep out the cold. Cheerful prospect.

Then a voice yelled, "General Houston!"

Sam heard the word spreading. "It's General Houston!"

Men waded toward him through the mud, reaching up to shake his hand.

"Thank God you're here, General Houston!"

"What's happened?" Sam asked dryly.

He got the story in snatches, men interrupting each other as they talked.

General Houston had been right. Santa Anna had come. What was more, he had done the impossible. He had marched through Mexico before the rise of grass. Lord only knew how many men he had with him. He had laid siege to the Alamo.

Sam made the air blue. Hadn't they blown up the Alamo?

No, a man said. They had no way to remove the sick. Johnson and Grant had taken all their horses, mules, oxen, and wagons. So the men had decided to hold the fort.

Yes, Colonel Bowie was there. But he was sick—bad sick. Colonel Travis was in charge.

They showed Sam a copy of Colonel Travis's letter, dated February 24:

Sow the Wind . . .

To the People of Texas & All Americans in the world—

Fellow Citizens & Compatriots—I am besieged, by a thousand or more Mexicans under Santa Anna—I have sustained a continual bombardment & cannonade for 14 hours and have not lost a man—The enemy has demanded a surrender at discretion, otherwise, the garrison are to be put to the sword, if the fort is taken—I have answered the demand with a cannon shot, & our flag still waves proudly from the walls—*I shall never surrender or retreat.* Then, come to our aid with all dispatch. If this call is neglected, I am determined to sustain myself as long as possible & die like a soldier who never forgets what is due to his own honor and that of his country—VICTORY OR DEATH.

"Where are Grant and Johnson?" Sam asked. "Marching on Mexico?"

No, the men said, that expedition had sort of petered out. Too many men refused to go.

Nobody knew for sure where Grant and Johnson were. Someone heard that they'd had an argument and split up. They were somewhere south of Refugio. Someone said they were hunting mustangs. The army was short of horses. Fannin was at Goliad.

"And he has five hundred men! Well armed!" a man said. "We're sure he's gone to help Travis! And five hundred men can hold the Alamo!"

"Man the walls around almost three acres of grounds? When would they get any sleep? And how can we keep them supplied?" Sam asked.

"We made copies of Colonel Travis's letter. We sent expresses on east with them. We've heard volunteers are marching toward Gonzales. Seventy or eighty miles from the Alamo. They'll organize there and—"

"Go to the Alamo? How will they get there? Santa Anna's army is being reinforced every day. You can be sure of that."

"What can we do, General Houston?"

"I have been removed from command," Sam said. "My only assignment now is to help organize a government."

One man exploded. "We kicked out that General Council!"

"What government is in operation now?" Sam asked.

"Uh . . . not exactly any," they admitted.

"Then we've work to do."

The next day the convention met around a long rough table in the unfinished building. They set to work to write a Declaration of Independence. On March 2— Sam's birthday—they signed it.

"Long live the Republic of Texas!" someone yelled.

"And the State of Texas is no more," Sam said. "So the commander in chief of its army resigns."

Men looked at him, startled. Didn't he understand

they had kicked out the General Council? It was the General Council that . . .

One delegate offered a resolution. The first order of business ought to be to elect a commander in chief of the army of the Republic of Texas! He smiled at Sam.

Sam got up. He reviewed the way the General Council had hamstrung his work. "We have no army. We have groups of men, here and there, with no organization. Before you elect a commander in chief, I have one suggestion! Decide what authority he will have. No man in his right mind would take on the responsibility of the job that lies ahead unless he had the authority to carry it out!"

The argument began: "We can't expect volunteers to obey a man they didn't elect. . . . Our president and his cabinet ought to have the right to say . . . After all, it's the . . ."

Robert Potter of Nacogdoches argued most hotly.

Finally all arguments were beaten down. The commander in chief would have *command!* Over all land forces—regular, volunteer, militia—or anything else that anybody thought of to call them!

They elected Sam—with one dissenting vote, from Robert Potter.

"And where *is* the Republic of Texas?" Sam asked. "Where is our constitution? Before we can be recognized by other countries, we've got to have an organization."

Mr. Ellis, president of the convention, divided the men into committees and set them to work.

Sunday morning, March 6, shouts of alarm brought all the delegates scrambling into the hall.

Mr. Ellis was white-faced. The letter in his hand was shaking. It was from the Alamo:

> We have contended for 10 days against an enemy force variously estimated from 1500 to 6000 men. . . . Col. Fannin is said to be on the march to this place but I fear it is not true, as I have repeatedly sent to him for aid and without receiving any. . . . I hope your honorable body will hasten reinforcements. . . . Our supply of ammunition is limited.

"The express said Colonel Travis had about a hundred and eighty men when he left. . . . The situation is . . . desperate."

Robert Potter jumped to his feet. "I move this convention adjourn and go to the aid of the Alamo!"

Men elbowed one another as they shoved toward the door.

"No!" Sam's bellow stopped them.

Fifty men of the convention against the Mexican army? That was senseless. Their job was to organize a government. Otherwise they were nothing but outlaws. It was *his* job to go to the Alamo. And—*as soon as his commission was written*—he'd go. He'd gather every available man—Grant's, Johnson's, Fannin's, the volunteers supposed to be near Gonzales. If humanly possible, he'd rescue the brave men at the Alamo. But the convention must finish its work!

Hockley and three others rode with Sam. They did not stop until late that night.

At dawn Sam walked away from the others and put his ear to the ground. Travis had said that as long as his flag waved over the Alamo, he'd fire signal guns at dawn and sunset. For a long time Sam listened. Heartsick, he got up. The guns were silent.

. . . and Reap the Whirlwind

The guns of the Alamo were silent. Had the Alamo fallen? Or had someone failed to fire the signal guns?

Sam leaped on his horse. "Let's go!"

Friday, as they approached Gonzales, they saw men camped near the town. Sam recognized Colonel Burleson, the experienced Indian fighter, and rode over to talk with him.

Almost four hundred men, Burleson said. No organization. Some with guns. Some not. Not enough ammunition even for those who had guns. About two days' rations on hand. He'd sent scouts to find out the situation at the Alamo. They ought to be back by tomorrow.

Sam asked that the men be paraded. They formed hit-or-miss groups in ragged lines. He read them the Declaration of Independence. They cheered. He read them his commission as commander in chief over all the forces. They cheered—after a fashion.

Sam wasn't surprised. He could remember the attitude toward "regulars" in the War of 1812. "Get them organized," he ordered. "Let them choose their own officers. Then—*start drilling!*"

He rode on into Gonzales. The people surrounded him. Did he have word from the Alamo? Did he know Fannin had not gone to help?

"Our men went," an old man said. "More'n two dozen. So Colonel Travis has over a hundred and eighty men now!"

"My boy went," a gray-haired woman said.

"My man went," a young mother said. "Just kissed me and the baby, picked up his gun, and marched off!"

A hundred and eighty men to hold the Alamo! Sam's throat ached. He talked with the people. He listened. He praised the courage of their men. The world would never forget the heroes of Gonzales, he said. He went back out to the camp.

He had not been there long when he heard a wild scream from the direction of the town. What in the name of—

Two mud-spattered Mexicans came racing toward the camp. "The Alamo! It is fallen! Every man killed! Santa Anna is coming! He will—"

The uproar in the camp drowned their words. Twenty men ran for their horses, jumped on, and fled.

Sam roared, "Send after them! Bring them back!" He turned, leveled a finger at the Mexicans, and roared even louder. "Arrest those men!"

"But, señor—"

"You filthy liars!" he bellowed. "Don't you think I'm on to your tricks! You're in the pay of Santa Anna! He sent you here to start a panic. Lock them up! I'll take care of them in the morning!"

Half a dozen soldiers grabbed the two, jerked them from their horses, and started dragging them away.

"Before God, señor—"

"Shut up!" a soldier yelled. "Or I'll knock your teeth right down your throat!"

Thirty men rode off to bring back the deserters. "At least," Sam thought, "I hope they'll bring them back—and not just keep going themselves!"

The hullabaloo in camp was quieting down.

Colonel Burleson spoke under his breath. "You sure those Mexicans are lying?"

"Almost sure they're not," Sam muttered. "But I didn't want half our men running and starting a panic. I need two scouts with fast horses."

"Yes, sir!"

Sam dictated the orders to Hockley. First to Grant and Johnson. He brought them up to date on the change of command and ordered them to join him immediately—by forced marches.

All the pieces of this army had to be pulled together.

"Two copies," he told Hockley.

A scout rode up. "Yes, General Houston?"

"We think Grant and Johnson have split up. That

they are somewhere south of here, down on the coast. Find them. But—take care of yourself! A live scout—who gets back with information—is worth more than a dead hero!"

"Yes, sir!" The man saluted, leaned in his saddle, and started at a gallop.

"Hockley, take this for Fannin," Sam said. Fannin was to blow up the fort at Goliad and come away immediately. They could expect both the Mexicans and the rising of the rivers any day. There was no time to be lost. Fannin was to bring away the guns if possible. If not, sink them in the river. "Inform him of the change in command. Get it off fast!"

When the second scout had gone to Fannin, Sam walked about the town cursing Santa Anna's foul trick in sending those lying Mexicans . . . and sizing up the number of wagons, carts, horses, oxen, and mules in the town. If the Alamo had fallen, he'd have to move the people out fast.

In the middle of the night he went to the jail to talk to the prisoners. At the sight of him they shrank back from the barred window as though even bars could not protect them.

"Before God, señor—" one began.

"Shhh!" Sam motioned for silence. "Forgive me. I had to stop the fright. Now, tell me everything you can."

The final attack had begun before dawn on Sunday, March 6. *Por Dios,* how bravely the men of the Alamo fought! But it was no use. Santa Anna ordered every man killed.

"They stacked the bodies, poured oil on them, and burned them!"

"All those brave men! Travis—Bowie—Crockett!"

"Davy Crockett?" Sam asked. "He was there?"

"*Sí*, señor. He came with his brave men. Not many, but very brave."

"When they marched into the Alamo, it was to put the head in the lion's mouth! Me, I could not be so brave!"

Sam took them back over their story again and again. How many men did Santa Anna have?

They weren't sure. At least seven thousand. More men came every day.

"Santa Anna flew the blood-red flag."

"It means *no quarter*—every man will die!"

"And when the Mexicans charged, they played the 'Degüello!' It is the song of death!"

When Sam was done questioning them, he picked up the crowbar he had brought and pried the bars from the window.

"Señor!"

"Your horses are east of the camp. Tethered alone. You must be far from here by dawn."

"But why, señor?"

"Then my soldiers will *know* you were filthy liars!"

They disappeared in the darkness.

. . . *and Reap the Whirlwind*

Sam went to the outskirts of the sleeping camp, spoke to a sentry, then walked off alone and sat under a tree.

Grant and Johnson might have three hundred men between them. Fannin had five hundred. With the four hundred men in camp he'd have over one thousand. Not all of them trained. Not even armed. He'd have to maneuver until he could get supplies. Keep out of Santa Anna's way until . . .

Those poor devils at the Alamo! He pounded his fist against the tree in helpless rage. Why, oh, why wouldn't that Council listen to reason? If he could have pulled all the forces together last December . . . But what was the use of saying Why?

He'd have to make do with what he had. Send out more expresses. Call for more men. If only those panic-stricken fools hadn't had a chance to bolt from the camp. If they got away they'd spread panic from here to Louisiana. If only . . . There was no use thinking that, either.

The next morning when the "escape" was discovered, Sam stamped up and down and roared some more about the filthy liars.

The men who had chased the deserters brought back about half of them. But at least ten men were fleeing east from Gonzales, spreading terror as they fled.

Hockley—Colonel Hockley now and inspector general of the army—came to Sam.

Good spirit in the men, he said, but they didn't know

the first principles of drill. If they had to fire three rounds to stand off an enemy charge, they'd probably all shoot one another. "But they don't see any use of drill. 'Fancy stuff' they call it."

"Maybe I can get something through their heads."

"I wish you luck, sir."

"Bring up three companies—one very green. That will be Company A. And be sure their guns aren't loaded!"

"That's easy, sir. Half of them don't have ammunition."

The three companies straggled over and stood in ragged groups. Sam thanked them for coming to the aid of their country. He knew he could depend on one thing. They were all good shots. If they weren't good hunters, they'd have starved to death, wouldn't they? The men nodded. A few began to grin.

"Now, we're going to demonstrate a battle situation," he said. "Company A, the other two companies are the enemy. They are going to charge. They have you outnumbered, two to one. How will you stand off the charge?"

"Mow 'em down!" a man yelled.

"That's the spirit!" Sam yelled. "Take aim!"

There were shouts of "Get over there! . . . Quit joggin' my elbow! . . . Get your head outta the way, or I'll blow it off!"

The noise stopped. The men looked at one another.

"Yeah. . . ." one drawled thoughtfully. "We gotta know where to stand so we got room to shoot, don't we?"

"Good for you! Now—suppose you all know where to stand—you have room to shoot—and the enemy is coming. Then what?"

"We mow 'em down!"

"Yeah! One big bang!"

"Fine! All right, enemy forces! Start coming!"

Company A went through the motions of "one big bang."

"Company B, fall out!" Sam ordered. "We'll suppose every man in Company A got a man with his shot. Company C, keep coming! Company A, fire again!"

"We ain't ready!"

"Go through the motions! Talk it off! Swab your guns—"

Company C rushed Company A, yelling in triumph.

"Hey, you know something, General?"

"What's that?" Sam asked.

"This durn business is like a square dance. We'd better know the figures!"

Sam shouted with laughter. "Good for you! I never heard it said that well before!"

They began to drill. Sam was watching them when he felt eyes boring through the back of his head. He turned and rode in that direction.

The scout he had sent to find Grant and Johnson was

back. A hollow-eyed, ragged boy was behind him on the horse.

"Follow me!" Sam led them away from the drill field. They stopped beneath a tree.

The scout dismounted and helped the boy from the horse. "I didn't have to go far," he said. "This one escaped. He was with Johnson. None of Grant's men got away."

The boy was weaving on his feet.

Sam dismounted and took his arm. "Let's all sit down."

"Thank you, sir." He sat with his head sagging forward. The smart uniform of the New Orleans Grays was in tatters.

Slowly he answered Sam's questions. Yes, Grant and Johnson had split up. Grant was ahead of them. So this Mexican general—Urrea—he was coming up from Matamoros and he caught Grant's men first. Nobody survived.

"I know," the boy said. "I heard Urrea's men talking."

Urrea had caught Johnson's men next. A few had escaped. Maybe twenty.

"I know Colonel Johnson got away. I saw him going."

"Where?"

"Just going."

"How many men did you have?"

"Grant—maybe a hundred. We had a little over a hundred."

So two hundred brave lads had been sacrificed to that fool scheme! Sam could feel the blood beating in his throat.

The boy must have sensed his anger. "I'm sorry, sir. But we did our best. We—"

"Lad, I'm not blaming you! I'm blaming the senseless fools who led you on that expedition!"

"I hear you're in command again, sir. I'm glad. I think you'll pull us through if—if it's not too late."

"Of course we'll pull through!" Sam got up and spoke to the scout. "Good work! Take care of him. And—both of you—keep your tongues between your teeth."

They nodded.

"My uniform?" the boy said. "If men ask if I was with Johnson?"

"You got sick and had to drop out. Understand?"

"Yes, sir. A lot of the men did drop out, sir. Some got sick. Some just got—disgusted. It wasn't anything like what we thought it would be."

"War never is," Sam told him. "There's only one reason why a man ever goes through what he goes through. Because of what he's fighting for!"

He helped the boy mount and watched them ride off. No help from Grant and Johnson. Nothing left now but the untrained men on the field, and Fannin's men. Thank God they were trained and armed!

Where were those scouts of Burleson's? They should be back by now from the Alamo!

Sunday morning. Still no word from Burleson's scouts. And no word from Fannin.

Burleson said, "Two fellows—probably the best scouts in the army—just joined us. Karnes and Deaf— only they pronounce it 'Deef'—Smith. How about sending them to get news of the Alamo?"

"Bring them here!"

Karnes was a young fellow in his twenties. Deaf Smith was almost fifty—short, red-headed, and very deaf from some childhood disease. Sam noticed that Deaf turned from one man to the other, watching each man's lips as he spoke.

Could Smith and Karnes get near enough the Alamo to find out what had happened—and get back alive?

Smith nodded. All he said in an odd, high-pitched voice was "Yup."

Would they need more men with them?

Smith answered that with one word, too. "Nope." He studied a minute, then explained with four words. "Just slow us up."

With the fastest horses in camp they set off toward the Alamo.

Early Sunday afternoon Karnes came pounding back, alone.

Burleson groaned. "No! We can't lose Smith!"

"Deaf's coming," Karnes said. "With a Mrs. Dickerson and her little baby. Couple of black boys with them, too. Colonel Travis's boy, Joe. The other's the fellow that Santa Anna is sending with a message for you, sir. Mrs. Dickerson's man died at the Alamo. They all did."

Sam sent fresh orders to Fannin. He could not wait longer at Gonzales for him. "We'll move out before midnight," he told Colonel Burleson.

"I'll do everything possible to—"

"*We move out!*"

Late Sunday afternoon three horses plodded into Gonzales with Mrs. Dickerson, Smith, and Santa Anna's messenger. Travis's boy, Joe, was on foot.

Joe recognized Sam, tried to speak, then turned away and began to sob.

People crowded the plaza, staring at Mrs. Dickerson.

She spoke in a flat, dead voice. "My husband was Captain Dickerson. He is dead. They are all dead."

For a moment there were gasps and sobs. Then women stood with their knuckles pressed against their lips, forcing themselves to be silent so they could hear what she said.

After a time the Negro on horseback spoke. "I'm Ben, sir. Colonel Almonte's body servant. My master is General Santa Anna's aide." He handed a letter to Sam. "From *El Presidente*, General Santa Anna, sir."

Sam stuffed it in his pocket. "Anything else?"

"General Santa Anna gave the men at the Alamo their chance to surrender. They refused. So—they all died. I am directed to say that that will be the fate of any Texan caught with a gun in his hands!" He bowed. "I have fulfilled my orders. I have escorted the lady here safely. I have delivered the message. Now I shall return."

One man reached for his gun, but Sam shook his head. Ben rode out of the town.

Mrs. Dickerson said, "Santa Anna said to tell the people of Gonzales he is coming by forced marches with five thousand men."

Travis's Joe looked around. "I saw that army! He's got more men than that! Nearer eight thousand!"

A murmur of sobbing began. Sam lifted his voice. "We leave Gonzales tonight! Be getting ready! Clothes —food. That's all—unless it's small enough to carry in your pocket!"

Tired with the all-day drill, without sleep, the army moved out at midnight. A rear guard waited to bring the settlers.

At dawn Sam called a halt. Only ten miles. They'd learn to do better than that. The men broke ranks, dropped in their tracks, and slept.

Hockley was with Sam when a scout came racing up. He was from Goliad. Fannin refused to obey. He had decided to hold Goliad. He had renamed it Fort Defiance.

Poor headlong fool! "Hockley, we'll never see Fannin again. Not unless he's on the move now." He looked over the ragtaggle army of half-armed, untrained men. "There is the last hope of Texas."

"The Last Hope of Texas"

Yes, here was the last hope of Texas. He could not make a stand on the Guadalupe. Texas had already lost over four hundred men. And Fannin's men didn't have a chance—unless they were already on the march.

With this last hope . . . Sam studied a map. The Colorado. That would be the place to make his stand. He would have to leave all the country west of it unprotected—but if he didn't keep this army from a massacre, all Texas was lost.

He sent an officer east to gather supplies and meet him on the Colorado. He must have arms, ammunition, cannons, mules to pull them, twelve good horses for his scouts, and food. In two days they'd be down to nothing but the cattle they killed.

Retreat. . . . He'd better explain to the convention at Washington-on-the-Brazos. He sent a letter:

> We could have met the enemy at Gonzales and avenged some wrongs, but, detached as we were,

without provisions, arms, ammunition, or artillery, it would have been madness.

He told of his plan to make his stand on the Colorado.
The men of the convention would please send expresses
on east, calling for men and supplies, to meet him there.

What was going on at the convention? Over a week
now since he came away. He had heard nothing.

A hundred men came marching up to join him. The
camp cheered. He gave the order to move east. The
cheering stopped.

Some of the men rebelled. They came to save the
Alamo. It was gone. They couldn't leave this part of the
country! They had families to take care of!

Fifty men—and their guns—disappeared that night.

More men joined him on the march. He'd have an
army yet! With arms and ammunition—and time to
train them . . .

It was raining almost steadily now. The little caravan
slogged through mud that was ankle deep. Rain. The
rivers would be rising.

Four days' slogging through mud brought them to
Burnham's Ferry on the Colorado. There, on the banks
of the swollen, raging river, Sam met the aftermath of
the panic-stricken flight of men from the camp at Gonzales. More than a thousand women, children, and old
men were milling about, begging to be taken across.

Soldiers recognized neighbors. They broke ranks and

rushed from settler to settler with frantic questions. "Where's Mary? . . . Did you see Mary?" "Where's my mother? You came right past her house, didn't you?" "Where's my wife? She *started* with you? *Where is she now?*"

A hundred men, without a word to their officers, started walking west. They were going to see about their families! Just try to stop them!

Sam rode among the settlers, trying to calm their fears. They'd all get across the Colorado, he promised. The soldiers would help. Not a soldier would cross until every settler was safe!

An express brought a letter to Sam. He recognized the handwriting and smiled. Tom Rusk was one of his best friends. One of the coolheads of Nacogdoches. A lawyer—brilliant, kindly, dependable. A man to bank on.

The convention was going ahead slowly, Tom wrote. But going ahead. They had elected officers. Sam smiled over two of the names. Tom Rusk was secretary of war. Lorenzo de Zavala was vice-president. But Sam did not smile at two other names. Robert Potter was secretary of the navy. And the president *ad interim* of the Republic of Texas was—David Burnet.

"I'm glad," Sam muttered, "that I hammered out the question of my authority! Burnet—if he could—would make more trouble than the whole General Council did!"

By the next day the settlers and the army were safely across the Colorado. Sam assigned a guard to take care of the settlers and sent them on east. The river was still rising. No sign of supplies yet. He moved downriver to Beason's Landing. From there he could guard three crossings.

Men were swarming into his camp now. His "army" grew to nine hundred men. Only it was not an army—just a mob of eager, determined men who wanted to lick the Mexicans. Sam directed his officers to get them organized and *start drilling!*

He sent scouts out for thirty miles upriver and down. He must know where the *Santanistas* were.

From time to time scouts brought in captured messengers. Sam began to get a picture. There were at least four armies coming east. They were spread out on a hundred-mile front, burning and looting as they came. Any one of the armies was big enough to outnumber his army two to one—if he had had an army. He didn't have one yet. How could he ever build one if men kept deserting? Just numbers was not the answer.

A scout who had ranged farthest north brought word about the convention. Someone had galloped through Washington-on-the-Brazos, yelling that the Mexicans were coming. The convention broke up and fled to Harrisburg on Buffalo Bayou. Everybody cleared out, the scout said. He thought maybe crooks had started the excitement—then looted the houses when the people fled. There seemed to be a lot of that going on.

"The Last Hope of Texas"

An express came from the convention-in-flight at Harrisburg. Stern orders from Burnet! The army must make a stand! They must not retreat any farther!

"My friend," Sam muttered. Once again he was glad he had hammered out the question of his authority.

He heard a commotion on the drill field and hurried toward the noise.

A Mexican was shouting. "It is true, señores! Fannin and all his men! Massacred at Goliad!"

Sam roared at the man. He threatened to have him shot. It was no use. The next morning there were only five hundred men in camp.

The next night Smith and Karnes came in from a scouting trip.

"This is it, General," Karnes said.

General Sesma was just west of them, getting ready to cross the Colorado. He had enough men to surround them.

Sam ordered the men formed into a hollow square. He rode into the center. His voice boomed:

"Fellow soldiers! The only army in Texas is now present! Travis has fallen with his men at the Alamo. Fannin's troops have been massacred at Goliad. There are none to aid us. There is but a small force here, and yet it is all that Texas has. We might cross the Colorado and attack the enemy. We might be victorious—but we might be defeated. There are but a few of us, and if we fail, the fate of Texas is sealed. For this reason, and until I feel able to meet the enemy in battle, I shall retreat!"

He let that sink in. Then he went on. If any man did not intend to stick, let him leave now!

No man broke ranks.

But Sam knew that some of the officers were muttering. Two of them, Baker and Martin, were spreading word through the camp: Another retreat, and there'd be a new commander in chief!

Sam ordered brilliant campfires lighted that night—enough campfires to have warmed the army he didn't have. Then leaving a rear guard to feed the fires, he moved east by forced marches, driving the men as he had never driven them before.

More men joined him on the march. Soon he'd have nine hundred again. But not an army! They reached the Brazos River. Baker and Martin were still talking about a new commander in chief.

Even the steadier officers asked for a conference. They had suggestions—all different. The army should make a stand here. It should cross the Brazos and make a stand on the eastern bank. It should go south. It should stay here. It should cross the Brazos.

"Gentlemen, if I listened to all of you, I'd be like the ass between two bales of hay. Remember? He couldn't make up his mind which one to eat. He starved to death. Thank you, gentlemen. You may return to your commands."

The next morning he gave orders to march north along the Brazos.

"The Last Hope of Texas"

Baker and Martin rebelled. Their men would not retreat!

"Excellent, gentlemen. I need brave men for very special duty."

They would hold the crossings on the Brazos—Baker at San Felipe, Martin on downriver. Were their gallant men willing to take on that dangerous duty? And—if the Mexicans came—destroy the ferries so the Mexicans could not cross?

The rebels marched off to obey.

The rest of the army started north. More men joined them. *If only there could be time to train them!*

It was raining more steadily now. Sam's officers were casting sidelong looks at the roaring Brazos. He could guess what they were thinking: Maybe we should have crossed it. . . . What if we're trapped on this side? . . . What if the Mexicans come and we're caught between them and the Brazos?

But Sam had seen the steamer *Yellow Stone* moving upriver. Riding high, as though in ballast, going for a cargo. Probably to Groce's Landing for a cargo of cotton. Jared Groce was one of the richest men in Texas. He would be ready to help—if Captain Ross of the *Yellow Stone* would agree.

But they must get there in time! Sam stepped up the pace of the march.

The *Yellow Stone* was just beginning to take on the load of cotton. Now—to talk to Captain Ross.

I can give orders, Sam thought, but what if the captain says No? He went aboard the *Yellow Stone*. "Captain Ross, I must take possession of the *Yellow Stone* in the name of the army of the Republic of Texas."

"At your service, General Houston! What can we do?"

"Stand by until I release you. I may make a stand on this side of the Brazos. I may need to cross. I'll not deny that, when the time comes, you'll be in danger. When I move, it'll mean the enemy is near. You'll be in danger on your downriver trip."

"All Texas is in danger, sir! Thank God you're in charge!" Captain Ross said. "We'll be standing by!"

Jared Groce came to shake hands and ask after the army. "I can't furnish arms and ammunition, but I can give you food. Help yourselves to cattle and corn. And set up your headquarters in my house, Sam. You look as though you could do with a little rest."

"Thank you, but I'll stay with the men."

He had to stay with them—to drill them. Once more he had a fine, eager mob—over half of them without any training.

He rushed off a plea for more supplies. More arms and ammunition. Cannons! Mules to pull them. Send everything on pack horses or pack mules. No wagons. He did not need any more wagons to wrestle out of the mud.

The rains were heavier. A good thing the camp was

on high ground. Soon it was an island, surrounded by rain-made lakes, swamps, and creeks.

In spite of the rain Sam drilled the men. He drilled them until they slumped in their tracks. They grumbled. They growled. They threatened. But they could not very well desert—not without wading in water up to their necks—or swimming.

One evening a scout brought in a sick-looking boy. He was so young the beard on his face was fuzz. "He was with Fannin," the scout said.

"Bring him to the supply wagon," Sam said.

There, protected from the endless beating rain, the boy ate, then talked.

"I can talk all right," he said. "No, I don't need to sleep first. I—I don't like to shut my eyes. I see things."

As he talked Sam could see things too.

The men at Goliad were fit and on their toes. Fannin was a good commander. Kept them up to the mark! They heard rumors of a Mexican army. Fannin sent about twenty men to bring in the settlers from Refugio.

"Double-time!" he ordered. "I want you back tomorrow!"

They looked very smart as they marched off. But they didn't come back.

Fannin sent almost a hundred men the next time.

At Goliad they waited . . . and waited. They stood on the walls of the fort and watched the road toward Refugio till their eyes ached. No sign of the men.

March 19 dawned with a gray-white fog that hid everything. It looked like the chance to escape. Fannin gave the order. His men marched out under the cover of fog.

But the fog that hid them could hide other things, too. Six miles out, Urrea's army surrounded them.

Fannin didn't panic. His orders were fast and firm. They formed a hollow square of their wagons, baggage—anything they could pile on the wall around them.

It was a hopeless fight from the beginning. The first day—sixty Texans wounded. They ran out of water. That was the worst of it. Hearing the wounded men in the night, begging for water.

Urrea had over one thousand men. The next day he got reinforcements.

Fannin surrendered. He and Urrea drew up the terms. All who laid down their arms would be treated as prisoners of war. They would be marched back to Goliad. As soon as ships could be found, they would be sent back to the United States.

It was cold in the fort. The guards took their blankets. The men lay on the ground. Even the wounded ones.

It seemed forever, waiting and waiting to go home. One night the guards brought in more men. They had just landed in Texas. Now there were over four hundred men in the fort. It was crowded. And cold.

"The Last Hope of Texas"

On Saturday night, March 26, they'd been there almost a week. They heard a rider come pounding up, yelling that he had brought orders from Santa Anna.

That night seemed very long. Some of the boys were pretty homesick. One had a flute. He played "Home, Sweet Home." Some of them sang. Some of them cried. The youngest ones.

But the next day they felt more cheerful. Nice day. Sunshine. Palm Sunday.

Then came the order, "Fall in!" They all cheered. They were going home! Some might be home by Easter!

All the able-bodied men lined up to march. What about the wounded? They'd be taken care of, a guard said.

They formed three companies and marched in three directions. Two rows of guards, one on each side of them.

The boy stopped talking. His teeth began to chatter. Sam waited. Finally he went on.

"After a while our guards yelled 'Halt!' Then we heard the clicks of the guns. Someone yelled, 'Boys, they're going to shoot us! Run!' I started to run. I stumbled and landed in a ditch. In some brush. I guess it covered me. I just lay still."

Again he stopped. Then he went on.

"I heard the shooting. Quick volleys at first. Then scattered shots from here and there. The guards were running down the men who tried to escape. After a long time I heard shooting back at the fort. I knew they were killing the wounded men, too. That night I started crawling. In the morning a man saw me. He was a Mexican, but he was kind. His family hid me. Then I set out to find our army—if we had any army left."

"And now that you've found us?" Sam asked.

The boy's eyes blazed in his white face. "I'm going to fight!"

"Good for you!" Sam reached out his hand. "Think you can do something to help me?"

"You bet!"

"When I ask you to do it, can you tell the men what you've told me?"

"You bet I can . . . sir!"

This, Sam thought, would be the test. Some men had fled at news of the Alamo. Some men had deserted at first news of the massacre at Goliad. The men who stuck after they heard this story—they were the men he could count on!

When the boy was stronger, Sam called in three companies. The boy talked to them. There was no sign of fear. They were fighting mad!

The story spread through the camp. The boy talked to others.

From that day on the men drilled without grumbling. They obeyed. They saluted with a snap. They were still so green and new to battle maneuvers that it was pitiful. But they were trying!

An express came for Sam from the president-in-flight at Harrisburg. Maybe—just maybe—news about artillery! Sam began to read:

> The enemy is laughing you to scorn. You must fight them. You must retreat no farther. The country expects you to fight! The salvation of the country depends on your doing so!

Siesta

Sam took a long tour of the camp before he tried to
answer Burnet. Finally he wrote:

> Dear Sir
>
> I have kept the army together under most dis-
> couraging circumstances, and I hope that a just
> and wise God, in whom I have always believed,
> will yet save Texas. I am sorry that I am so wicked,
> for "the prayers of the righteous shall prevail."
> That you are so I have no doubt, and I hope that
> heaven will help and prosper you.

When he had sent that letter he sat with his head in his
hands. There was no doubt about it. Burnet was trying
to oust him.

The next day an express, about to leave camp with the
mail, came to Sam. "Sir, you check all the mail before it
leaves camp, don't you?"

"I do."

The express handed him a fat letter. "I feel like maybe
you didn't see this one, sir."

Siesta

Sam took the letter. It was addressed to Secretary of the Navy Potter. He flipped over to the last page. A Lieutenant Perry. Yes. He had joined them at Beason's Landing—with a high recommendation from Potter.

Sam began to read. In response to Secretary Potter's request, Mr. Perry would report on the condition of the army under Houston.

Shocking conditions, according to Mr. Perry. No discipline. No training. It seemed to be true that General Houston had not had a drink since the beginning of the campaign. Some thought he was probably using opium.

Sam glanced up at the express. "You may go." He went on reading. When he had finished, he sent for Lieutenant Perry.

Mr. Perry's eyes widened when he saw the letter in Sam's hand. One by one Sam read the lies, pausing after each one. "So, Mr. Perry?" After two pages, he stopped.

"What is the purpose, Mr. Perry? To stir up enough doubt in the Cabinet that they will depose me?" No answer. "If I read these lies to the men, Mr. Perry, what do you think would happen to you? I'm afraid you would be found dead, Mr. Perry. Some unfortunate accident."

Mr. Perry was looking a little green.

"Now, Mr. Perry, suppose you *get to work!*"

Mr. Perry departed on the double.

The next day both Lorenzo de Zavala and Tom Rusk joined the camp.

"Come to see conditions for yourselves?" Sam asked.

They denied that. They had come because they thought they could do more good fighting than hiding!

The rains still marooned them. Sam went on with the drilling. If only he could have at least six weeks with these men!

A scout raced in. Martin's outpost at Fort Bend had failed. They couldn't hold the ferry. They didn't destroy it. An army had crossed. At least a thousand strong! All eastern Texas was in a panic now. The president and his cabinet were fleeing to Galveston.

Sam rushed scouts to all the outposts with the order: Cross the Brazos! Join the army at Donoho's Farm!

He wrote a dispatch and had copies made to send to the men all over east Texas. Men must not panic when they heard that the Mexicans had crossed the Brazos. *The enemy was treading on the soil where he would be conquered.* If men of Texas wanted to save their land and homes, they would stop this flight! They would join the army! Now was the hour!

Then Sam called for the *Yellow Stone*. He had nine hundred men to cross the Brazos. With nine hundred men he could meet any Mexican army of one thousand men! He could—

The camp doctor came to him. "Bad news, sir. We have a hundred sick men. I've ordered—"

"What is it?"

"Measles. Some are mighty sick. If it spreads through the camp it will be serious."

"It'll be disastrous!" He went to see the men. Some

were listless. Some were swearing. Some were weeping with rage because they'd miss the fight.

He swore with them, ordered the hospital enlarged to take care of them, and left sixty men to guard them. Those men almost wept, too.

"You want to leave helpless men to Santa Anna's butchers?" he asked.

They calmed down and promised to stay on guard.

Hour after hour the *Yellow Stone* chugged across the Brazos with the army—minus the hundred sick men and their guards.

On the east bank of the Brazos the men saw supplies.

Then someone gave a shout. Cannons! Finally! Two fine new six-pounders! Gifts from the people of Cincinnati! The cheering men named them The Twin Sisters.

Then their cheers died. Where was ammunition for the cannons? They hunted frantically through every box. Not . . . one . . . lousy . . . cannon ball!

"We'll make shot," Sam told them. "Grape and cannister!"

He set the men to gathering every scrap of old iron they could find. In the blacksmith shop on the farm he showed them how to cut up the iron scraps and fill small bags.

"When we fire that—and it scatters—better than cannon balls!"

Some newcomers joined them here. Sam beamed. He might get back up to that nine hundred men yet!

Sam was still busy at the blacksmith shop when a new recruit strode up and thrust a gun in his hand. "A broken lock! Fix it! On the double!"

Sam gave a sidelong glance and saw a group of soldiers watching. He saluted the recruit. "Yes, sir! On the double. Come back in an hour."

Half an hour later the recruit dashed up, stuttering. "S-s-s-sir! I b-b-beg your pardon, sir. They told me, sir, that you were a blacksmith, sir!"

Sam roared with laughter. "I am! I'm a damned good blacksmith. Here's your gun. On the double."

His laughter spread to the listening men. He was glad. They could do with a little laughter.

A Negro came into camp and asked to see General Houston. He had been captured by Santa Anna, he said, and had been freed to bring a message to the Texans. Santa Anna with a thousand men had crossed the Brazos. He would march on Harrisburg, destroy it, and then he'd "smoke out" that General Houston who had been running from him like a frightened rabbit!

Was it possible? That Santa Anna would advance that far into enemy territory with only one thousand men?

"Get ready to march!" Sam ordered.

If only the rain would let up! But the rain, that had sometimes drizzled and sometimes poured, now came down in torrents. Sam led the march to a ridge of land, not quite so water-soaked, and drove the men without mercy. Those three days of forced marches were the

toughest ordeal his men had yet faced in the long retreat.

Karnes and Smith joined Sam, and brought a captured messenger. He carried letters from General Cos to
Santa Anna. General Cos was coming by forced
marches.

That night Sam studied a map. One more crossing to
make. Buffalo Bayou. It followed a twisting course east
into the San Jacinto River. The mapmaker indicated
marshes and swampy land along the south bank of
Buffalo Bayou. Sam thought of the cannons and shook
his head.

They reached the north bank of the Buffalo Bayou—
flooded now, running over 350 feet wide and 15 feet
deep. No crossing it without a ferry.

A camp doctor reported, "Bad news, General Houston."

More men down with the measles—at least 150.

And Cos was coming by forced marches to join Santa
Anna. When Sam left another 150 men here—and men
to guard them—he would have fewer than 800 men.

He ordered a camp set up for the sick. He asked for
volunteers to guard them. Not a man spoke. They had
come to fight! Sam smiled. It was the spirit he needed
now. But—the sick men had to be taken care of. He
assigned men.

From here on, he told his men, they'd travel light.
Leave everything possible behind in this camp.

They slogged east to the ferry—and found it abandoned. Men checked and reported back. "Bad news, sir."

It was hopeless. Leaking. Half full of water. About to sink.

Sam dismounted and pulled off his coat. "Let's get to work."

"Sir?"

"To stop the leaks! We're going to use that ferry!"

They cut planks and got the worst of the leaks stopped—for the moment. They started across with the first load. A plank came loose. Water poured in. The men fought to get back to shore before the boat sank.

"Have to do better," was all Sam said. He fixed that plank himself.

The boat was drifting badly with the current. They'd be rowing three times the distance to get across once. Sam called for everything that could be turned into a rope. It took a long time to make a rope long enough and strong enough to hold the ferry. Too long!

If Santa Anna should attack from the south and Cos from the north . . .

At last the rope was ready. With that reeved through the pulley to hold the boat from drifting . . . and if the planks held . . .

They stationed men to bail, loaded the boat as heavily as they dared, and started again. Sam went with the first load and asked Tom Rusk to bring up the rear.

It was dusk when the last man reached the south shore.

Siesta

Sam called the men together. He rode into the center of a hollow square and talked to them. The hour they had waited for was near at hand. Santa Anna, the butcher of the Alamo and of Goliad, was at their mercy! Cut off without support! (He didn't mention the army coming by forced marches to join Santa Anna.) There was going to be a fight. Some would die. If any wanted to drop out, now was the time.

He waited. Not a man moved.

"Then I give you a battle cry!" he yelled. *"Remember the Alamo! Remember Goliad!"*

Hundreds of voices roared back. "Remember the Alamo! Remember Goliad!"

He yelled again, and the men answered. Their eyes blazed. They'd need that fire before this night was over!

This march, he told them, was going to be the hardest one yet. Santa Anna would head for Lynch's Ferry. He would try to cross over into eastern Texas, and march on, burning and killing as he went.

They had to beat Santa Anna to Lynch's Ferry. It would be impossible—for any men but Texans! But they were Texans! And they had a battle cry!

The roar went up again. *"Remember the Alamo! Remember Goliad!"*

They started through the swamps and marshes south of Buffalo Bayou. They sank in up to their knees—to their thighs. They slipped and sprawled. The Twin Sisters sank in the muck. They had to dig them out.

A little solid ground—then a gully in the darkness.

More swamp. Little streams that they sank in up to their waists. More solid ground. More swamp.

Sam drove his men till they dropped in their tracks. He let them sleep two hours, then ordered them out again.

They came at last to a sizable stream flowing into Buffalo Bayou. Vince's Bayou. Running brimful, too. The bridge was already under water at one end.

At last they stopped. They were on a rise of ground, where Buffalo Bayou flowed into the San Jacinto River. Behind them, to the east, was Lynch's Ferry. South of them they saw the Mexican army. They had won the race!

Sam ordered the men to eat and rest. He sent a scout with field glasses to climb a tall tree and look over the Mexican camp.

The camp was beyond a rise of land, the scout said, just where the slope leveled off. The Santanistas had a barricade of wagons, boxes, saddles, and everything across it. There was a cannon in the center. Big one. Maybe a twelve-pounder. Stacks of ammunition for it. Cannon balls by the hundred! Looked like they had lots of everything. Pretty good-sized army. Lots of tents. The camp was pretty well protected, too. Water behind it, swamp to the east. Only way to hit them would be to charge that barricade. Right into the muzzle of that twelve-pounder.

Sam thanked the scout. He settled down to study his

map again. Yes, Santa Anna, "the Napoleon of the West," as he liked to call himself, was well protected. Water behind, swamps to the east. . . . Sam smiled grimly. Texans to the north, and the only escape by Vince's Bridge. The "Napoleon of the West" had himself in a pocket!

The Mexicans were alert and spoiling for a fight. Sam refused to start a battle.

He sent the cavalry to reconnoiter. The officer in charge disobeyed, engaged in a brief skirmish, and got into trouble. One man killed, another wounded and thrown from his horse. Mirabeau Lamar, a dashing chap of French descent, swooped down and rescued the fallen man.

Sam stormed. He removed the commander of the cavalry, promoted Lamar from private to colonel, and put him in charge. If any other man wanted to disobey orders . . .

The men muttered, but they finally settled down.

That night a blue northern howled over the camp, driving the temperature down almost to freezing. But the day dawned bright and clear, and gradually the sun warmed their bones.

The men were at breakfast when a picket shouted. Hundreds of reinforcements were joining Santa Anna's camp!

Tom Rusk shot a startled look at Sam.

Sam got up, shrugged, and said, "Probably that same

old trick." He looked toward a rise of land that hid all of the men but their heads. "Yes, same old trick. They're just marching around in a circle behind the hill."

He beckoned to Deaf Smith and told him to go check on the situation. Reinforcements, or just a trick? As always, Deaf Smith watched Sam's face intently as Sam talked. Sam let one eyelid fall in a slow wink. He hoped Smith saw and understood. The scout gave no sign. He lifted his hand in his usual sketchy salute and ambled off.

Presently he came back grinning. He made quite a speech—for him. "Just like you said, General. All humbug. Fellers marching round and round below that hill." Then Smith's eyelid fell in a slow wink, too. He strolled away.

Presently Sam joined him.

"Cos and his men, all right," Smith said. "About six hundred, I'd guess."

Sam nodded to a tree on the west edge of the camp. "There are axes there. Good and sharp. Take some men —with plenty of muscles—and ride for all you're worth to Vince's Bridge. Cut it, burn it—anything—but get rid of it. Then—you'd better get back fast or you might miss something."

Smith's grin was from ear to ear. "Sounds right interesting, General. We're on our way!"

Sam called together his top officers and Secretary of War Rusk for a conference. He told them of the reinforcements under Cos. What should the Texans do? Attack? Or defend?

He asked each man in turn, starting with the two youngest ones.

Both of them said, "Attack, sir!"

But all the other officers and Secretary Rusk said, "Defend!"

Santa Anna's troops would be the pick of the Mexican army. The Texans were raw and untrained. They would have to cross almost a mile of prairie to reach the barricade. Who could expect raw troops to hold steady under that?

Sam listened, nodded, and asked, "Is there anything else?"

Two officers spoke of Vince's Bridge. It was their only escape back to the west. One end was already under water. Wouldn't it be well to build a floating bridge to cover that end?

"An interesting idea, sir." Then Sam got up. "Thank you, gentlemen. Return to your commands. And, until further orders, I want this camp quiet! *Quiet!*"

The sun climbed to twelve o'clock high, then began to slide west. Sam watched it. Two o'clock . . . three o'clock . . . *siesta time. . . .*

"*Remember the Alamo!*"

Siesta time . . . "when no Latin-American would do anything but rest." Sam got up and sent for his top officers.

"Fall in. Keep quiet. Pass the word."

Silent, puzzled, the men fell in. Sam gave them their orders. They would march in columns of two, then left, forming one long line straight across the prairie, only two men deep. They would be marching up a slope. If they kept low they would not be seen very easily until they topped the slope. Then they would be almost on the Mexicans.

"Remember! Keep low, move fast, and hold your fire till I give the command! I'll wave my hat—like this—and yell 'Fire!' "

Did they have a drummer?

Yes, a boy said. He couldn't exactly roll the drum, but he could beat it like the dickens.

Did they have a fife?

Four boys stepped forward. They had played some together, they said. They could play "Come to the Bower I Have Fashioned for You" just fine.

"Remember the Alamo!"

Sam smiled to himself. Very fitting for siesta time.

"Remember! Not a sound out of you till I yell 'Fire!' Then *cut loose!*"

Marching in their long line, just two deep, the Texans started up the long slope of the prairie. Sam rode back and forth in front of them.

"Hold your fire! Keep low! Hold your fire!"

The Twin Sisters were in the center of the line, a little forward of the men. The cannons sank into the soft ground. The sweating men cursed as they dragged the heavy cannons up the slope. They'd better be worth all this trouble! They'd just better!

Finally a sentinel in the Mexican camp shouted a warning to the Santanistas. The Texans could hear shouts, yells, and commands.

"Keep low!" Sam yelled. "Hold your fire!"

A volley blazed from behind the barricade, but the shots were high, and went over the heads of the advancing Texans. Bullets did strike Sam's horse. Sam leaped aside in time to keep from being pinned under it when it fell.

"Hold your fire!" he roared. "Damn you, hold your fire!"

A cavalryman brought him a horse. He mounted and raced in front of the line again. "Keep low! Hold your fire!"

The Twin Sisters boomed, opening a breach in the barricade.

"Hold your fire!"

And the Texans, green and untrained as many of them were, obeyed. Keeping low, absolutely silent, they came on.

Another volley from the Mexicans. A few Texans fell, but most of the shots were still too high. Sam felt something slam into his right boot, then his leg went numb. His horse staggered, but was still on its feet.

At last, when his men were close enough to make every shot count, he waved his hat and yelled, "Kneel! Fire!"

The Texans fired one murderous volley.

"Forward! Charge! *Remember the Alamo! Remember Goliad!*"

Drumbeats, a shrilling fife, and a savage yell, "*Remember the Alamo! Remember Goliad!*"

The Texans charged. Some went through the break in the barricade. Some leaped over it.

Sam's wait for siesta time had paid off. He caught the Mexicans completely off guard. Some were asleep, some playing cards, some leading their horses to water. The sentinel's warning yell aroused the camp. But it was too late. Before they were ready for battle the Texans were upon them with that savage yell. Officers tried to rally their men. But the rage of the Texans was too much to face.

Mexican soldiers knelt, pleading, "*Me no Alamo! Me no Goliad!*"

The fight lasted less than half an hour. Some said eighteen minutes. The Mexican forces broke and fled. Some fled east—but there was no escape. Only a swamp that could swallow a man—even a horse and rider. Some fled west—but Vince's Bridge was down.

Sam felt the horse beneath him stagger again. He leaped, landed on his left leg, tried to take a step, then stopped. He remembered the slam of the bullet against his boot.

He yelled for a horse and managed to mount. He roared at his men. "Fall in! Fall in!"

They could not—or would not—hear him. They had scattered in every direction, chasing the fleeing Mexicans.

If reinforcements reached Santa Anna now, the Texans wouldn't have a chance! Sam bellowed orders. He might as well have talked to the wind.

At last his officers got their men under control. The killing stopped. The Texans began to herd Mexican prisoners toward their camp to the north.

Sam started back across the prairie. The ground was spinning. Hockley caught him as he fell from his horse, laid him under an oak tree, and called for Dr. Ewing.

Surgeon Ewing cut off Sam's boot and examined his leg. "Both bones splintered above the ankle. This is going to hurt." He got the bullet and some splinters of bone. "We've got to get you to a hospital where we can—"

"I'm not going anywhere!" Sam snapped.

"But why?" Dr Ewing asked. "It's all over. You've

won the fight. The Mexicans are completely routed. Hundreds dead. More hundreds prisoners."

"Where's Santa Anna?" Sam asked.

No one had seen him.

"Find him!"

If Santa Anna had escaped, the victory meant nothing. There were four other armies in Texas. Any one of them had enough men to wipe out the Texan forces. If Santa Anna escaped and rallied those armies . . .

Where was Santa Anna?

The Texans were still wading through the tall grass beyond the battlefield, hunting for fleeing Santanistas. They searched until dark. No sign of Santa Anna.

The next morning Thomas Rusk brought the battle report to Sam. For the Mexicans—over 600 dead, over 700 prisoners, over 200 wounded among the prisoners. For the Texans—7 dead or mortally wounded, about 30 others wounded. It was unbelievable!

But where was Santa Anna?

Sam ordered men out in every direction to continue the search. "You'll find the Napoleon of the West," he said, "making his retreat on all fours. And he will be dressed as poorly as a common soldier. Examine closely every man you meet!"

Hours passed. Now and then a Texan rode in, herding a prisoner or two in front of him. Now and then a Santanista came in by himself, his hands raised in surrender, carrying a slip of paper. A searcher had sent the prisoner in alone, and had gone on with the search.

Sam swore at that. "I want these prisoners *brought* in, not *sent* in! Until we have Santa Anna, not one man must escape!"

"They ain't going to escape, General," Deaf Smith said. "They ain't got anywhere to go. They'll get swallowed in the swamp or drowned in the bayou." He grinned. "Vince's Bridge is down!"

But Sam went on muttering. The hours dragged. His leg was hurting like the very devil. Dr. Ewing was fussing about it.

"We've got to get you away from here! Or this leg—"

"Hang my leg! We've got to find Santa Anna!"

Afternoon passed. The shadows lengthened. The searchers brought in fewer and fewer stragglers. Some returned with no prisoners.

One last group of searchers came in, with one lone prisoner riding behind one of the Texans. A big catch for a day's hard hunting they growled. They rode to the "corral" where Texans were guarding their captives.

A Mexican prisoner looked up. *"El Presidente!"*

A Mexican officer tried to silence the man. It was too late. The shout ran through the Mexican prisoners: *"El Presidente!"*

And a shout went up from the Texans. They had captured Santa Anna!

The Texans brought the prisoner to where Sam lay under the tree. The prisoner bowed, his hand on his heart, and spoke.

Sam knew a little Spanish—enough to guess at the words.

"I am General Antonio López de Santa Anna, president of Mexico, commander in chief of the Army of Operations. I place myself at the disposal of the brave General Houston."

Inch by inch Sam hitched himself up until he was sitting, leaning against the tree. He took his time about it. He knew the mood of his men. He had heard the shout of triumph—then the guttural sound of their fury. One bellow of rage from him, and a dozen men would shoot Santa Anna.

That must not happen. Santa Anna must live. He was the only man who could order the other Mexican armies to retreat.

"If you ever held your temper," Sam told himself, "do it now!" He motioned to a nearby box and invited Santa Anna to sit. "Hockley, I'll need an interpreter."

"I thought of that, sir. Young Major Zavala is coming."

Young Zavala came. He stared at Santa Anna. His face was blank. Was he remembering that Santa Anna had put a price on his father's head?

Apparently Santa Anna was going to try to forget it. He hurried to Lorenzo. Sam could guess at those words, too. "My friend! My friend! The son of my old friend!"

Lorenzo's bow was formal. "It *has* been so, sir."

"This won't do," Sam told Hockley. "Get Colonel Almonte, Santa Anna's aide. He speaks English."

Hockley hurried away.

"Thank you, Major Zavala, but I can't ask you to be my interpreter now. It's going to be hard enough for *me* to hold my temper. I can't expect it of you."

"Why should you hold your temper, sir?"

"Because if I don't, someone will shoot Santa Anna."

Lorenzo spoke with deadly quiet. "I'd like the honor. He deserves to die!"

"But he's got to live. He's the only man we can bargain with."

"But . . ." Lorenzo hesitated, then bowed. "Yes, sir!" He saluted and walked away.

Hockley brought Almonte. Sam waited until Almonte and *El Presidente* had time to exchange a volley of Spanish.

Then he said, "Colonel Almonte, you will please interpret for us." "And you, Sam Houston," he said to himself, "will hold your temper!"

Santa Anna began with a flowery compliment. The man who had conquered the Napoleon of the West was no ordinary man! He was a man of destiny. Now he would be as merciful as he was brave.

Merciful! Sam got a grip on himself before he spoke. "You should have thought of mercy at the Alamo."

Santa Anna shrugged. He had given the men their chance. They had refused to surrender. Besides—a gesture of his hands said how helpless he was—he had been acting under the orders of his government.

"Who gives orders to a dictator?" Sam asked.

Santa Anna insisted. He had positive orders. He was to kill every man in Texas found bearing arms. To treat all such as outlaws. That was all they were. They had no government. They were fighting under no recognized flag.

Sam thought of the day at Washington-on-the-Brazos when he had shouted down the move to adjourn the convention. When he had insisted they stay and form a government.

"We do have a government. We'll probably be able to make a flag. If you think you had an excuse for the slaughter at the Alamo . . ." He had to stop. He could feel the blood pounding in his ears and the cold sweat running down down his face. He waited till he had a grip on himself. "If you think you had an excuse for that, what is the excuse for the massacre at Goliad? Those men laid down their arms. They surrendered. They were promised that they'd be paroled."

General Urrea had no permission to accept a surrender, Santa Anna said. The orders of the government had been positive. All men found bearing arms would be executed.

Sam could feel a wave of cold hate crawling through the listening Texans.

"Before we talk longer," he said, "you will write orders to General Filisola and direct that all Mexican armies draw back to the Rio Grande."

Santa Anna tried to protest. Sam waited without answering. At last Santa Anna wrote the order.

Sam did not trust Almonte to translate that. He sent for Major Zavala.

"Yes, sir!" Lorenzo's eyes glowed. "It is quite satisfactory!"

Sam ordered Deaf Smith to carry the orders to Filisola, and a force of Texans to follow and see that the orders were carried out. He ordered Santa Anna's tent brought and pitched near the tree where they were talking. Everything—the tent, the bed, the rugs, the bottles of champagne, the silver dishes, the trunks . . .

Again that guttural sound of fury. His men were growing more sullen by the minute.

"General Houston," Almonte said, "perhaps you can answer one question. Why didn't you attack on the twentieth? Before we got reinforcements? You knew General Cos was coming, didn't you?"

A gasp from the startled Texans, then silence.

Sam spoke loudly enough for his voice to carry quite a distance. "Yes, Colonel Almonte, I knew you'd get reinforcements. But I reasoned this way: Why take two bites of one cherry?"

A half-chuckle from the Texans. Almonte's eyes blazed.

Sam raised his voice again. "Sir, it would not matter

how many reinforcements you had! You can't conquer free men!" He pulled a big ear of dried corn from his pocket and held it up. A few grains had been shelled from it. "Sir, I've lived off this ear of corn for the last four days!" He waved it. "Do you think you can conquer free men? When their commander can march four days on one ear of corn?"

A cheer went up from the Texans.

"General Houston!" a man yelled. "Give us that ear of corn! We'll plant it! Every blessed grain! We'll call it 'Houston Corn'!"

Sam grinned. "Take it along. Give every man a grain as long as it lasts. Plant it. But don't call it 'Houston Corn.' Call it 'San Jacinto Corn'! For the bravest men who ever won a battle!"

The cheer spread through the camp. Sam heaved a sigh of relief. He had given his men something else to think about—at least for the moment.

Almonte said, "General Houston, *El Presidente* wishes to arrange terms for his release."

"I can't deal with him. I'm not a dictator. We have a constitutional government—with a president and a cabinet. They'll have to deal with him."

"But where *are* they?"

Sam wished he knew. They had fled to Galveston. They might be there, aboard a ship, ready to flee the country. Perhaps they had already fled. He only said, "They'll be here presently."

That night Sam, Tom Rusk, and Hockley prepared

dispatches to send in every direction. To the Texans fleeing east toward the Sabine: Texas was saved. They could return. To New Orleans and other points in the United States. A special one for President Jackson. One for President Burnet and his cabinet, with a report of the battle and a request that he come immediately to deal with Santa Anna.

That report must go to Galveston Island—about forty miles as a crow flies. But they had only one rowboat—a leaky one at that—for a man to use to cross Galveston Bay.

"We'd better send three men," Rusk said. "Two to row and one to bail. And I, for one, wouldn't order men to risk that boat! I'd rather ask for volunteers."

Sam grinned. "No use. Try it and see what happens."

The next morning Rusk did. He explained the need to reach Galveston Island—the risk of the leaky boat. He asked for volunteers.

A shout shook the trees. "Send me! . . . I'll go! . . . Send me!"

Rusk silenced them. He smiled. "Gentlemen, I know now what General Houston meant. He said it was no use to ask for volunteers."

The men grinned.

One drawled, "No, sir, that boat won't hold all of us. And the ones that goes, they'd better be good swimmers. Take me now, I'm good."

Three men were chosen—tough, wiry, hard as nails, and all good swimmers.

The camp saw them off with jokes and laughter. After they had gone, though, a silence settled. Any man there was ready to face the risk—but they all knew the risk it was.

A week passed. No sign of Burnet and his cabinet. April ended. May began. Still no word. Had the messengers ever reached Galveston Island? Or had they been drowned? If they had reached the island, what had they found? Had Burnet fled the country?

By May 3, twelve days after the battle, Sam's leg was swollen to twice its size and red streaks were running up the leg from the wound.

"We've got to get you to a hospital!" Dr. Ewing said.

Sam tried to fight the pain and dizziness. "Not till Burnet comes."

"Listen, you!"

"Get Hockley."

Hockley came.

"I'd better do a letter for Burnet while I can still think straight," Sam muttered.

He lay with his eyes closed. The words came slowly. One by one he listed the conditions he felt must be carried out before Santa Anna was released.

1. Mexico must recognize the independence of Texas.

2. The boundary of Texas would run from the headwaters of the Rio Grande to its mouth.

3. A commission from . . .

Sam's words were coming more slowly. Hockley had to lean close to hear the rest of the conditions.

"... Not a Chance!"

May 5, two weeks after the battle of San Jacinto, the *Yellow Stone* chugged up. Burnet and Robert Potter came ashore first.

Burnet had nothing to say to the man who had won the battle. Where was Santa Anna? He stalked away, followed by his cabinet.

"What the devil?" Hockley muttered.

"Did you give him my letter of conditions?" Sam asked.

"No, sir. I—I—was too dumfounded to think."

"Take it to him. Before he starts dealing with Santa Anna."

Hockley went. He came back, shaking his head. "Not a word! Not a word about the victory! I did learn one thing, though. The *Yellow Stone* goes back to Galveston Island day after tomorrow."

"Good!" Dr. Ewing said. "We'll send you down on her, Sam, and get the first ship to New Orleans. I only hope we're in time to save . . . that leg."

It seemed to Sam he had held on to consciousness as

long as he could. "The army. Brigadier General Rusk will take over."

"Brigadier General?" Rusk asked.

"You've just been promoted. Tell Burnet to appoint a new Secretary of War. The army . . ."

Sam knew he could not talk to them. Time was when his bellow could reach a thousand. Not now.

Hockley took down his farewell. Sam finished in a whisper.

". . . The enemy, though retreating, are still within the limits of Texas. . . . Let not contempt for them throw you off your guard. . . . When liberty is firmly established by your patience and your heroism, it will be enough to say, 'I was a member of the Army of San Jacinto.' . . . My heart embraces you with gratitude and affection. . . ."

On May 7 the *Yellow Stone* got up steam. Tom Rusk and his brother carried Sam on a cot to the landing.

President Burnet stalked up. "Where are you going?" He listened. "Oh, no! *Mr.* Houston resigned his command. Therefore, he has no right to travel on this vessel. The *Yellow Stone* is engaged in government service."

Two members of Burnet's cabinet, one on either side, helped the president block the way—Secretary of the Navy Potter and the new Secretary of War. Mirabeau Lamar—the private that Sam had promoted to a colonel —had taken Rusk's place on the cabinet.

Captain Ross came over. "What's the trouble? General Houston not coming? Oh, but he is! The *Yellow Stone* is not sailing without him!"

Burnet glared. He opened his mouth and shut it again. Perhaps he was afraid he was stepping on the toes of authority he did not understand. "Very well. Bring *Mr.* Houston aboard." Then he wheeled to confront Dr. Ewing. "You, sir! Where do you think you're going?"

"With General Houston. Someone's got to take care of him!"

"Leave this ship, or you are dismissed from the service!"

"Then I'm dismissed," Ewing said. "Captain Ross, may a doctor in private practice—and just now out of funds—have passage on your ship?"

"Not sailing without you."

At Galveston Dr. Ewing went in search of passage to New Orleans. The *Liberty*, one of the ships of the little Texas navy, was there.

"My destination?" the captain said. "To New Orleans for repairs."

"Thank God!" Dr. Ewing said.

Both Burnet and Secretary of the Navy Potter said "No!" *Mr.* Houston had left the service. A naval vessel would not carry him to New Orleans.

A beat-up little American schooner, the *Flora*, was lying off Galveston.

"Passage for General Houston?" Captain Appleman

said. "Of course there's passage for General Houston!"

"We can't pay you now," Dr. Ewing said. "But—"

"The devil with paying me now! The *Flora* will be proud to have him aboard! Only wish the *Flora* was a finer ship!"

The captain of the *Liberty* sent a man to talk to Sam. They could get General Houston aboard the *Liberty* in secret and—

Sam refused. "Texas is not a military despotism. That's what we've been fighting about. Neither the army nor the navy can defy the civilian government."

Dr. Ewing got Sam aboard the little *Flora*.

"We'll get you to New Orleans in jig time!" Captain Appleman promised.

Contrary winds delayed them. They waited . . . and waited.

Captain Appleman came to Sam one day, grinning and shaking his head. "General Houston, your soldiers certainly are back of you, heart and soul. And the new men, landing from the United States, too. That—that— Burnet said something—well—*sneery* about you, and you ought to hear the uproar! It'd do your heart good! Wouldn't surprise me if they dumped Burnet and his cabinet in Galveston Bay!"

"No! *No!*"

"Huh? I thought you'd be—"

"Get Dr. Ewing! Tell him to bring pencil and paper!"

". . . Not a Chance!"

The doctor came. "Sam, nothing is worth your—"

"Take this down!" Sam whispered fiercely.

To the Armies of Texas

The Commander in Chief has heard with regret
of some dissatisfaction that exists in the army.
If it is connected with him or his circumstances,
he asks as a special favor . . .

When he finished he lay a moment panting and sweating. "See that it's delivered immediately."

"With *pleasure*, sir!" Dr. Ewing snarled.

It was Sunday, May 22, a month after the Battle of San Jacinto, when the *Flora* reached New Orleans.

Word of her coming had alerted the city. Sam, lying on the deck in a feverish daze, could hear a band playing.

Men came with a stretcher.

"No! Let me stand!" He stood a moment on his homemade crutches. The cheering stopped in a long-drawn gasp. A woman sobbed. Someone said, "Oh, how *awful!*" Then everything blurred.

When he wakened he was in a clean bed, in a clean room, between clean sheets. How long since he had been clean?

Two men were looking down at him. He recognized his old friend, William Christy. The other man—something familiar about him. Then the other man scowled, just as he had scowled about twenty years before. Sam knew him.

"Well, Dr. Kerr, we meet again."

"I guess Old Hickory was right," Dr. Kerr said. "The good Lord *must* have something for you to do. Didn't think you'd make it. It's been touch and go, my friend."

"You mean—how long have I been here?"

"A week."

"But I've got to get out of here! I've got to—" He tried to sit up. He felt Dr. Kerr's hand shoving him back. . . .

When he looked up again only Dr. Kerr was by him.

"I must have dozed off."

"That was yesterday," Dr. Kerr said. "Listen to me, Sam Houston! And get this through your head! You're not out of danger yet! You're not going anywhere for at least two months!"

"Are there any letters for me?"

"If I let you have them, will you promise to obey orders?"

"Yes, yes! Give me the letters!"

Things were in quite a turmoil. Soldiers were swarming in from the United States. They had got there too late to fight for Texas, and now they were making trouble.

Sam fumed.

"Remember your promise!"

". . . Not a Chance!"

Sam muttered and lay still.

The next news was worse. Burnet had made two treaties with Santa Anna—one public and one secret. And he had promised to send him back to Mexico so he could carry out the secret treaty!

Santa Anna had been on shipboard, ready to sail. Unruly soldiers, just in from the United States, had threatened to overpower the crew, capture Santa Anna, and shoot him.

Burnet had had Santa Anna removed from the ship and imprisoned somewhere "for safekeeping." So the terms of the treaty had been broken.

"If Santa Anna is executed," Sam said, "Texas will never live it down! I've got to get back!"

"It'll be August before you move one step from here!"

The middle of June, in spite of Dr. Kerr's warnings, Sam started back. The doctor had been right. Sam didn't get as far as Nacogdoches. In the little town of San Augustine, east of Nacogdoches, he had to give up.

In August he was still sitting with his leg on a stool most of the time. And by August, Texas was in another turmoil. September 5 would be election day. Texans would vote "Yes" or "No" on the constitution and annexation to the United States. No trouble there. They'd vote "Yes"! The turmoil was over the race for president. Stephen Austin was one candidate. Ex-Governor Henry Smith, the peppery little man, was the other.

Friends came to Sam. "You've got to run for president."

Sam's doctor pounded a table. "No! He's still a sick man! Hasn't he done enough for Texas?"

"He won't have to campaign. Just say he's a candidate. He won't have to take office till the second Monday in December. And the first president only serves two years. Not three."

"If he says he'll run, I'll spread it around that he's not fit to serve! Runs a temperature. Not always in his right mind!"

"Doctor, Sam is the only man who can save Texas. Henry Smith belonged to the War Party. He hates Austin like poison. Whichever man wins, it's going to split this country wide open. You understand, don't you?"

The doctor said, "No!"

Towns began to hold mass meetings, nominating Sam. People signed petitions: General Houston for President!

Finally, less than two weeks before the election, Sam said "Yes."

"Why, Sam, why?" the doctor pleaded. "What chance does Texas have? Over a million dollars in debt from the war. Indians on one side and Mexico on the other. Personally I don't think Texas can go it alone."

"I don't either!" Sam said to himself. "Annexation is our only chance." Aloud he said, "And people didn't think we could win the war, either."

The doctor snorted. "Humph! That war wasn't a

patching to what lies ahead. You haven't seen the men who've been flocking into Texas. Some good men—sure —but a lot of the most thoroughgoing rapscallions I've ever seen!" He sighed. "I wish I thought you'd lose the election."

Sam won in a landslide. The vice-president was Mirabeau Lamar. Sam remembered the dashing figure Lamar had cut on the battlefield. But keeping Texas on even keel wouldn't be done with gallant dash. That was going to be a long haul.

The constitution did not state when Congress would meet. President Burnet called it into session in October, in the little town of Columbia, on the Brazos River.

The capital of Texas had followed the fleeing President several places during the war. Now, for no reason Sam could figure out, it was at Columbia. Perhaps because Santa Anna was imprisoned nearby, and Burnet thought the government should keep an eye on him.

Congress met October 3. Sam moved to Columbia to keep in touch with things. He wouldn't take office until December, but he'd probably have to work with Burnet's Congress. He could get around some without his crutches now, but he was glad he had till December.

The morning of October 22, 1836, men called on Sam. Burnet had resigned. General Houston would be inaugurated that afternoon.

Columbia did not even have the "town hall" of Washington-on-the-Brazos. Ceremonies began under a huge live oak tree. It began to rain. Ceremonies continued in a storehouse. Sam took the oath of office on a blanket-covered table.

He didn't talk long. There was much that needed saying, he told the people, but this inauguration had come up rather suddenly. He would have more to say later. Presently he paused. He unfastened his sword. "It now becomes my duty to make a presentation of this sword —the emblem of my past office. I have worn it in the service of my country. Should my country call, I expect to resume it."

The people stood to cheer.

Sam did not sleep much that first night in office. He sat staring at a letter that had come from Washington, D.C., and trying to plan a way out of an impossible situation. He read it again:

> . . . not a prayer of a chance that the United States will annex Texas. That would mean another slave state. The North will fight it tooth and nail. I doubt if President Jackson will even recognize our independence. I think Congress will vote him down.

Sam tried to sleep, but the words beat through his head: not a chance . . . not a chance . . . not a chance.

"Indian Cunning"

Sam's first nominations for his cabinet raised half the eyebrows in Columbia. His two opponents for the presidency: Henry Smith for secretary of the treasury and Stephen Austin for secretary of state. Austin refused. He was too tired. He just wanted to go home and rest.

Sam sent his name in nomination to the Senate. The vote was unanimous. "You can't refuse now," Sam told him. "You've never said 'No' when Texas needed you, and she's never needed you worse than she does now!"

"All right . . . Sam."

Sam could not remember that Stephen had ever called him that before. "Thank you, Stephen. I need you. Oh, Lord, how I need you!"

They shook hands and set to work.

Sam talked with Lorenzo de Zavala about a place on his cabinet.

Zavala smiled but refused. "I am going home to my family. I have been too long away."

Sam didn't urge him. He thought of the glow in Señora Zavala's eyes when she said, "God has been good to us. We are together."

And Columbia would be no place for Zavala to bring his family. Columbia, Sam thought, was no place for man or beast!

Zavala promised he would come again—maybe in six months—not before! "*Adios*, señor!"

November 20 a letter came from young Lorenzo. His father was dead. He had died November 15. He had been out in a boat with his little three-year-old son. The boat had overturned. Zavala managed to put the little boy on the overturned boat and push the unwieldy hulk to shore. The strain and exposure had been too much. He had died of pneumonia.

Sam spent a long time over two letters. The one to Lorenzo was hard to write. The one to Señora Zavala was much harder.

Stephen Austin was crushed. Zavala had been his long-time friend. "It's left a *lonesome* place" was all he could say.

Sam wished he could take time to go see the Zavalas. But he could not leave Columbia now. Not until he had solved a few problems.

First, he must get Santa Anna out of Texas alive! The Senate passed a resolution to keep him imprisoned. The army talked of overpowering Santa Anna's guard and shooting him—after a trial, of course.

If Texas did not honor the treaty with Santa Anna, she could never hold up her head among nations. Sam hammered at the Senate. Finally he got them to agree that the president could "use his judgment" in dealing with Santa Anna. Sam was glad of that. He had already started "using his judgment." Santa Anna was on his way to Washington, D.C., to talk with President Jackson about Texan independence. From there, President Jackson promised to send him home to Mexico.

Sam and Stephen wrote various letters-of-state to send by Hockley and the other escorts of Santa Anna. Sam wrote one letter for Hockley to deliver to Old Hickory:

> My greatest desire is that our country Texas shall be annexed to the United States. . . . It is policy to hold out the idea (and few there are who know to the contrary) that we are very able to sustain ourselves. . . . Yet I am free to say *to you* that we cannot do it.

With Santa Anna on his way, Sam turned to other problems. An unruly army of over two thousand men— how he could have used that help during the war! Contractors cheating on supplies for the army, raids by Indians, threatened invasions by Mexicans.

He spent all Christmas Day at a table in the bare little shack that was the "Presidential Palace," trying to work through a stack of problems that had no answers.

Toward evening Stephen Austin's servant came. Marse Stephen was sick! Bad sick!

Sam went to the bare shack that was the residence of

the secretary of state. Stephen was burning with fever, and delirious.

In spite of all Sam and the doctor could do, Stephen grew weaker. Two days later the doctor said, "Not much longer. . . ."

Stephen opened his eyes and his smile flashed. "Texas recognized! Did you see it in the papers?"

And he was gone.

Sam wrote a general order of mourning for all Texas:

> The Father of Texas is no more. The first pioneer
> of the wilderness has departed. General Stephen F.
> Austin, Secretary of State, expired this day at half
> past twelve o'clock at Columbia.

After the service for Stephen, Sam came back to Columbia. Stephen's death, too, had left a lonesome place.

Sam would be glad when the capital moved out of this miserable spot!

Two promoters, the Allen brothers, had the approval of Congress for a plan. They would build the capital of Texas on Buffalo Bayou, not far from the battlefield of San Jacinto. Congress promised the capital would remain there a certain number of years. The Allen brothers promised to have everything ready by May 1, when the next Congress convened. "Houston City" was already a very impressive city—on paper. Fine wide streets. Squares and rectangles marked off showing the Capitol, the Presidential Palace, and the Halls of Congress.

"Indian Cunning"

By the middle of March Texans were planning big things for April. They would celebrate San Jacinto Day in their new capital. Maybe, they said, they would celebrate annexation to the United States, too. Why was it taking so long to arrange for annexation? Hadn't they voted for it, clear back in September? Hadn't President Houston sent William Wharton to Washington, D.C., to arrange everything?

Sam listened and said nothing. He knew now there was no chance of annexation. Judging from Wharton's last letter, there wasn't even a chance that the United States would recognize Texas as an independent country.

It was near the end of March when Sam got the news. Mail was slow from Washington, D.C., to the village on the Brazos. Wharton had at least gotten the United States to recognize Texas as an independent country. He had managed to have a simple little item attached to a bill, a provision to vote funds for a representative to the Republic of Texas "when the President of the United States felt that Texas was ready for recognition."

President Jackson signed the bill and—on March 2— appointed a chargé d'affaires to the Republic of Texas.

Nothing but recognition? Texans were baffled. What did they have to *do* to be annexed?

"Settle down," Sam told them. "Plant crops. Keep the peace! Get a treaty of peace with Mexico."

Sam moved to Houston City the middle of April, 1837. The fine wide streets were mud roads, still dotted with stumps. The Presidential Palace reminded him of his first home in Tennessee—two log cabins and a dog trot. Only these cabins weren't so well built as their cabins in Tennessee. Nor so well furnished. Each cabin had a rough table, a cot, and a tick filled with Spanish moss.

A friend told Sam of a newcomer to Texas—Dr. Ashbel Smith. Brilliant fellow, trained in both medicine and law, in the United States and Europe. "I'm going to bring him around, Sam. I hope you can persuade him to stay. Texas could use a few men like that."

Dr. Smith was slim, wiry, with a dark beard and lively dark eyes. No, he said, he hadn't made up his mind yet if he'd stay.

"Use the guest quarters of the Presidential Palace while you make up your mind!" Sam led the way across the dog trot to the other cabin.

Dr. Smith studied the cot, the tick, and the table. What was he thinking about? Finally he spoke. "What if I said I preferred the Presidential Suite to this mere guest room?"

Sam shouted with laughter. How long since he'd done that? He hoped Dr. Smith stayed a while. He needed someone to laugh with.

After a few days Sam found that Dr. Smith was a good man to discuss problems with, too. Right now Sam was puzzling over what in heaven's name to do with the army. Not the old reliables from the San Jacinto campaign; the headlong, headstrong glory-seekers who had swarmed into Texas after San Jacinto. They were making more trouble, Sam said, than the Indian raids and Mexican threats put together. And a certain Felix Huston—spelled without an *o*—was a ring leader in the trouble. Felix-the-Great, Sam called him.

"I think I call him that because I hate to call him Huston—even without the *o*. He's a natural-born leader. The soldiers would follow him to Timbuctoo if he said the word."

In one of the shuffles in the army, Felix had been in temporary command. Made a brigadier general.

"I sent in a good man to take over as senior officer. Felix challenged him to a duel. The poor devil accepted the challenge. He was badly wounded. So Felix is still in charge. Heaven knows what he'll stir up next."

Two days later they heard. Felix-the-Great wás talking up an invasion of Mexico! First to Matamoros! Now—when the most important thing for Texas was a peace treaty with Mexico!

Sam walked the floor and swore. "Matamoros again! I've got to stop it!" He paused. His eyes narrowed. He looked at Dr. Smith. "And I think I can stop it—with your help."

Dr. Smith listened. He stroked his beard. "You really think it will work?"

"If I know those soldiers like I think I do."

Soon Felix-the-Great swaggered into Houston City, the special guest of the president. He even occupied the

Presidential Suite. Sam slept on a tick on the floor in Dr. Smith's room.

While Sam was busy, Dr. Smith talked with Felix. Dr. Smith was deeply interested to hear all about that expedition to Matamoros. How many men? What arms and ammunition? What supplies? How many wagons? Ah, ha! Pack mules instead of wagons, eh? Dr. Smith nodded. He could see that this young officer had a head on his shoulders! Everything very carefully thought out. Now what about a medical corps?

Presently Felix smiled. "You're not fooling me, you know. I know what's up! Our do-nothing president is coming around to my way of thinking! He just hates to admit it!"

"Amazing!" Dr. Smith said. "Generally men of your type—the handsome, virile ones—aren't such deep thinkers!"

That night Sam lay on his tick until snores told him Felix-the-Great was asleep—probably dreaming of the conquest of Mexico.

Sam got up, whispered to Dr. Smith, then left the cabin. He wakened Secretary of War Fisher and talked with him.

"You think it will work?" Mr. Fisher asked.

"If I know those soldiers like I think I do. So—get to that camp as fast as you can. I don't know how long Dr. Smith can keep our dashing brigadier general entertained."

"Indian Cunning"

When Secretary of War Fisher rode into camp, word spread like wildfire. Hurrah! Their gallant commander had persuaded the president!

They fell in. They saluted. They listened. They stared at Mr. Fisher, baffled.

The president was granting the army a thirty-day furlough. Just a skeleton force would remain in camp. The furloughed men would march to assigned locations all along the shore. The president wanted them to enjoy their furlough. They would be very busy on their return.

Mr. Fisher smiled. "You know how it is in armies in Europe? In Sweden and places like that? The army builds roads, clears land, drains swamps—all sorts of duty. Excellent idea. Keeps the men fit. Is a great help to the country."

Any man, he said in closing, who did not return immediately when recalled *would be branded a deserter and dealt with accordingly!*

When Felix-the-Great returned to his post, his army had departed. About six hundred old reliables remained. The newcomers had all set sail for home.

The outraged shouts of Felix echoed from San Antonio to Houston City.

"I hear," Dr. Smith remarked one day, "that this 'half Cherokee blackguard of a president is full of Indian cunning.'"

"What do you think?" Sam asked.

"I think—I'll cast my lot with Texas."

"Good! I need a surgeon general for the army. You seem to have the right feeling for a military post."

The only trouble, Sam thought, was that he'd miss having Dr. Smith around. He didn't have many people to laugh with. Nor much to laugh about.

Sometimes he was glad the first president's term was for only two years and that he could not succeed himself. By the fall of 1838 he might have a feeling that he ought to run again and fight some things through.

"But I can't—thank heaven!" he told himself.

The summer of 1838, though, he admitted to himself he'd have given his shirt—his *hair* shirt—if he could have run again.

Mirabeau Lamar was running for president—and on the platform that he would give Texas "a new character"! No more of this penny-pinching do-nothing! A big army! A big navy! Trade with foreign countries! More money! Lower taxes! No more kowtowing to "Houston's pet Indians"! He'd settle *that,* too!

Sam groaned. The Senate had steadily refused to ratify the treaty he had made in '36 with The Bowl and his Cherokee Indians.

The Bowl and his warriors had honored the treaty. There had been peace on that border.

But if Lamar won the election . . .

Margaret

There was anti-Lamar sentiment in the presidential campaign. There was opposition. Too much, Sam was afraid. If the other two men split the anti-Lamar vote, Texas would get that "new character." Sam wasn't sure she'd survive it.

Either of the opponents was a better prospect for president, Sam thought. The older man drank too much, but no one doubted his ability or his honesty. The younger man—Sam knew him well—was a moody fellow sometimes, but even in his darkest moods he never forgot his manners. Both of them lawyers. Both brilliant men. If only one would drop out and throw his votes to the other!

Then the older man—he may have been drinking when he did it—committed suicide. In spite of his shock and regret, Sam had a feeling of relief, too. Now the vote against Lamar wouldn't be split!

Then the younger man—in one of his dark moods—committed suicide, too. Sam was stunned. Why didn't I see it coming? he asked himself. Why didn't I help him? How did I fail?

Lamar walked into the presidency unopposed. His vice-president was David Burnet. They were in complete agreement. They would give Texas "a new character."

Sam had not known how tired he was until he laid down the load. He had tried to win annexation—and failed. He had tried to complete the peace treaty with Mexico—and failed. He had tried to get the Senate to honor the treaty with the Cherokees—and failed.

He knew he had accomplished some things. And some of the things he had started would go on. Young Pinkney Henderson, special Texas agent in Europe, was doing a beautiful job. He had written a trade agreement with England. He was in Paris now. Other nations were asking to talk with him. Paris liked him so much they had asked President Lamar to keep him on. President Lamar was glad to. There weren't many young men with his talent who were rich enough and interested enough to support themselves in Europe and work for Texas!

Yes, some things were started and would keep on, in spite of "the new character." Just now Sam could turn his mind to a life of his own. He'd develop the ranchland he owned, pick up his law practice—James Prentiss and his associates were ready for a lawyer in Texas now. But first—he'd have a vacation!

He wrote Old Hickory when he'd come to visit him at The Hermitage. Just a brief stop in New Orleans and another stop in Mobile, Alabama. William Bledsoe, a well-to-do young broker, was interested in Texas land. But a day in Mobile would take care of that.

Sam tried to express for himself what William Bledsoe was like. He had a—a leisurely sort of charm. Mr. Bledsoe was delighted to meet General Houston. He was very much interested in Texas land. But why should they sit around in an office to talk? General Houston must come out to Spring Hill. He must meet Mrs. Bledsoe. He must pay them a little visit.

Sam thought of Indian treaties and of Latin-American siestas. He said he'd be charmed to see Mr. Bledsoe's home and to meet his wife. He could stay for the night.

Mr. Bledsoe's carriage gleamed. The horses were perfectly matched. They started out the road.

"Nonsense!" Mr. Bledsoe said. "You must stay longer than overnight! At least a week!"

They turned into the drive at Spring Hill—and chattering voices and laughter rose like five orchestras tuning up.

Mr. Bledsoe groaned, but smiled, too. "General Houston! I forgot! What I've done to you! Emily is having a lawn party. You'll have to put up with being lionized by at least three dozen perfectly charming creatures who never stop talking."

Emily Bledsoe filled the description of "perfectly charming." She sparkled. She clasped her hands. "General Houston! Spring Hill is honored! You are the most famous man who ever *has* been here! You must make us a nice long visit!"

In a moment more charming young women were flocking around, filling the air with their compliments. They had heard *so much* about him! That wonderful, wonderful battle! And someone had seen him when he got to New Orleans! He had looked perfectly *awful!* Everybody thought he'd *die!* And . . .

Sam bowed over hands and wondered how far back into his past these charming creatures knew of Sam Houston. Back to the days when he refused to explain why he resigned as governor of Tennessee? And had been burned in effigy? Back to the months when he turned his back on life?

Emily Bledsoe was bringing four more sweet young things to swell the chorus, when Sam smothered a gasp. Nothing but his Indian training could hide the way he felt. Behind him he heard the only voice in the world that had ever reminded him of his mother's voice. The only voice that was as beautiful as hers had been.

He wanted to turn, but Emily was saying, "And *this* is Mary Lou Whitman! Just the sweetest girl we know! And—"

Sam bowed over more hands, smiled, and hoped he was saying the right things.

Then Emily said, "Oh, Margaret! Here you are! I've been looking all over for you! General Houston, this is my dear sister, Margaret Lea."

Margaret

Sam turned. The tall girl with black hair and sooty black lashes over clear gray eyes smiled at him and held out a dish of strawberries. "I come bearing gifts." It was the voice he had heard.

Sam got mixed up in which-hand-for-the-dish and which-to-bow-over. He found he was holding her left hand in his left and bowing over the right hand—and the dish of strawberries. He switched things around and almost spilled the strawberries.

"Now," Margaret said, "if I'd just bring you a glass of punch for the *other* hand, you could have a lovely time trying to eat the berries, couldn't you?"

"Margaret!" Emily pretended to be shocked. "That's *General Houston!* You can't talk to him that way!"

Sam wanted to say, "Please keep on talking!" But he had a feeling that if he spoke he'd stutter. Margaret *Lea* . . . Mr. Bledsoe had talked of his mother-in-law, Mrs. Nancy Lea. Margaret must be *Miss* Margaret Lea. . . . Why couldn't he say something? Why did he stand here like an oaf, looking into her smiling eyes?

Luckily Emily filled the gap. "I told General Houston he must pay us a nice long visit! And I shan't take 'No' for an answer."

Sam found his voice. "I'll be delighted."

Someone was calling. "Margaret! Margaret Lea! We want you!"

She spoke with mock sternness. "Steady with those strawberries!" and she was gone.

"Isn't she darling?" Emily said. Then, without waiting for an answer, "Now, let me see. Who else—"

"I want to hear about you!" Sam told her.

"Oh, General Houston!"

"You're much younger than your sister, aren't you?"

"Oh, no! Only two years. I'm eighteen!"

So Margaret was twenty. . . . Only twenty. . . . And he was forty-six.

"Your husband tells me your mother is quite a personality."

Emily's laughter bubbled. "Indeed she is! Father was a Baptist minister. When he died, Mother just took over. Ran the family, of course. *Some* people said she ran the church, too!"

So Margaret was the daughter of a Baptist minister. . . .

That evening the family gathered and Margaret played her guitar and sang. Old songs Sam had heard long ago.

Emily beamed proudly. Between songs she said, "Margaret plays a piano and a harp, too. Plays like an angel! Don't you think she sings like one? Just like an angel? And she's the brainy one! Studied *Latin* and things like that! And she can write poetry, too. Perfectly beautiful. Sometimes it makes me want to cry! You must think I'm very silly."

"I think you're delightful," Sam told her, and meant it. "I'd like to have you for a little sister!"

"Oh, General Houston, what a perfectly darling thing to say!" She was about to go on, but Margaret was singing again.

Only twenty. . . . Sam tried to think of Jim Bowie and his happy marriage. Of the Zavalas. He looked around the stately room. He thought of the raw new towns of Texas—the homes that were two log cabins and a dog trot.

But people had not thought his mother could face the life in Tennessee. Mother had said, "I hope I have as much starch as my grandmother had!"

Later Emily suggested that Margaret show General Houston the azalea path and the "perfectly darling" moon.

Margaret went down the path laughing softly. Sam decided he was supposed to laugh, too. Then he talked with Margaret.

Yes, she said, her mother *was* "quite a personality." Her laughter was loving. "People adore her—but they step when she snaps her fingers! Sort of a Roman matriarch, Mother is!"

And Margaret was only twenty. . . .

Mr. Bledsoe praised Emily for persuading General Houston to make them a visit. How about it? Would General Houston be willing to address some audiences in Mobile? They were interested in Texas.

Sam would be delighted.

Mr. Bledsoe always introduced Sam with a flourish. "Ladies and gentlemen! The hero of San Jacinto!"

People always gave him a standing ovation.

As Sam talked he always found his gaze coming back to a pair of glowing, black-fringed eyes.

If only he could stay longer! But he had written Old Hickory once and put off his visit.

His last night in Spring Hill Sam walked again down the path with Margaret and sat on the bench. "Do you believe in love at first sight?" he asked her.

It seemed forever before she answered. "Yes. Because that was the way I fell in love—a long time ago."

Sam's heart was in his boots. "A long time ago?"

"Three years."

"Did 'love at first sight' last?"

"Yes."

"I hope you get to see him often."

"No."

"Where did you meet him?"

"I didn't meet him. I just saw him. But I've never forgotten it. . . . It was May twenty-second, eighteen thirty-six."

Sam's heart was pounding now.

"He was the raggedest, dirtiest, wildest looking man I ever saw. He stood for a moment on the deck of the *Flora*. Then he fainted. I thought he was dead." She shivered. "I thought he was *dead!*"

"Margaret!"

Margaret

Then doubts began to gnaw at him. The life in Texas . . . Margaret's mother . . .

Margaret must think about it, he said. He would come to her home on his way back to Texas. He would meet her mother. He would write to her from Tennessee. Would she answer his letters?

"Of course."

At The Hermitage Old Hickory said, "Took you long enough!" But he didn't ask questions. He shook his head over the prospect of annexation. Not a chance. The North was too bitter about it. Maybe someday, somehow, something would change the mood. He didn't know when or how or what!

Sam wrote to Margaret. He waited for her answer. . . . She wasn't going to answer! She had thought it over and decided the whole idea was crazy. . . . She *had* answered, but her letter was lost. . . . *His* letter had gone astray, and she had not heard from him!

Her letter came. He began to smile with the first line. He smiled all the way through. Then he read it over again.

On the way to Margaret's home in Marion, Alabama, Sam wavered between hope and black doubts. He knew Margaret loved him. But what about her family? And her "Roman matriarch" of a mother?

"General Houston," Mrs. Lea said, "sit down and let

me look at you. You put a body's neck out of joint when you're standing."

Sam had never had anybody study his face so intently. He felt as though Mrs. Nancy Lea could peel off each layer of his mind and read them, one at a time.

What was she thinking about? His unhappy first marriage? His months as Big Drunk? According to his enemies, he was still Big Drunk. Had "never drawn a sober breath." Just how, Sam wondered sometimes, could he have done all the work he had done if he had "never drawn a sober breath"?

How much longer before Mrs. Lea was going to say anything?

At last she spoke. "If you had been a Baptist minister, General Houston, do you know the kind you'd have been? A real old 'hell-fire' preacher. That's the kind."

Sam didn't know whether it was a compliment or not, but the others were laughing, so he laughed, too.

Mrs. Lea had little to say about their engagement. Just "If Margaret is sure."

He wondered what the good people of Marion would say about Margaret marrying "that Sam Houston." He wished he could stay in Marion long enough to prove to them that "that Sam Houston" was not as black as his enemies painted him.

But news from Texas was bad. Lamar had launched his fight against "Houston's pet Indians." He had started a war with a trumped-up charge against the Cherokees. His army had killed The Bowl and driven the people—men, women, and children—across the Red River to take refuge with Oo-loo-te-ka.

Filled with shame over the betrayal of the Indians, Sam went back to Texas. If only there were something he could do! But it was all over now. The Cherokees were driven from their land, and the speculators were splitting up the acres. A good thing, he thought, he had opened his law office in San Augustine. He wouldn't get much business in Nacogdoches.

He wondered how his partner, John Birdsall, was getting along. A real lawyer, John! They'd often laughed over Sam's six-months' study. They made a good team!

As he rode into San Augustine a friend hailed him. "Glad you're back, Sam! We've elected you to Congress—representative from San Augustine!"

"Why?" Sam asked. "Because you knew Nacogdoches wouldn't have me?"

"Durn it, no!" the man insisted. Then he added, "But, anyhow, we wanted you."

"Thank you! When Congress convenes I'll be in Houston City ready to—"

"Hadn't you heard? Lamar's moved the capital. Up on the Colorado. Little settlement around there called Waterloo, or something like that. The new capital is named Austin. I hear tell it's beautiful country."

"Yes," Sam agreed. "Beautiful country. And they couldn't have picked a better name. But—what a location! A day's ride from any other settlement. Exposed to Indian raids—and Lamar is stirring up the Indians. Then there's a little matter of honor. When Congress bargained with the Allen brothers, they promised the capital would stay there awhile. Or doesn't that matter?"

"Don't get mad at me, Sam!" the friend pleaded. "I didn't move the capital. I just told you about it."

"Sorry. All right. When Congress opens, I'll be in Austin."

"Start early. If the roads are bad, it'll take you five days from Houston. And do they have a time hauling supplies! An ox cart makes about one trip a month." The men started off, then turned back. "Mighty sorry about your partner, Sam."

"What!"

"You hadn't heard? Died of yellow fever. Just like that."

Sam went to the office and found dust on everything. At the inn he got a bundle of letters that should have been answered a month ago. He worked until almost dawn. If he had to attend that session of Congress . . .

Then a thought hit him. The plans for the wedding! He wrote to Margaret. William Bledsoe and her mother were coming to Texas to look at land. Could she come with them? And they could be married in Texas? Please send her answer to Austin, he said.

He sent the letter, and tried to remind himself of how long it would take to get an answer.

When Congress met, the new representative from San Augustine took his seat. He pulled out a piece of soft pine wood and a clasp knife and began to whittle. Fellow members shot sidelong glances at him. They whispered behind their hands. Word passed down the line. Sam Houston was carving an Indian head! What was he up to?

Day after day Sam left a little pile of shavings under his seat. Not a word out of him. Just Indian heads.

Then one day he started talking. The Republic of Texas had waged war against the Cherokees and had driven them from their lands. Whether the war was just or unjust—and he believed it had been unjust—the deed was done.

The Cherokees had given up their lands.

But—to whom did the lands belong now? To speculators who had been seizing Cherokee lands before the war? Surely not! No individual had any right to seize any of the lands. All the Cherokee lands should become public lands, belonging to the national government of Texas. The government should survey the lands and offer them for sale. The money received for the lands should go to the treasury of the Republic of Texas.

When that was done, the sale of the land would help the national government and all the people of Texas—not just speculators.

Wasn't that the right thing to do? Surely no honorable congressman could want it otherwise, could he?

The debate went on for days. Sam whittled. He made an amazing number of Indian heads.

Finally the House voted—for all Cherokee lands to become public lands of Texas. How could a man go on record against something that would benefit the whole nation?

Sam folded up his knife and dusted off the shavings. He headed for Galveston. William Bledsoe, Mrs. Lea— and Margaret—were due to arrive there soon!

Sam had not talked of his engagement, but waiting at Galveston, he could not help telling friends about it. His bride-to-be was on that ship—right out there—waiting for a pilot!

The wait was too long! Sam hired a dory and went out to meet the ship. As he went on board he saw William Bledsoe and Mrs. Lea. But . . . He looked around.

"Where's Margaret?"

William Bledsoe spread his hands in a helpless gesture and turned away. Mrs. Nancy Lea stared at Sam with a stony face.

Linsey-Woolsey President

Where was Margaret? Sam looked at William Bledsoe's back, at Mrs. Lea's stony face. He found himself praying silently, "No, God, no! Don't let anything happen to her!"

He wet his lips and asked again, "Where's Margaret?"

Mrs. Lea stood stiffly erect. "Sir, my daughter is at home, where she belongs. She will not go chasing forth in the world to marry any man. The man who marries her will come to her home!"

Sam was so relieved he could have kissed Mrs. Nancy Lea. But—what was he going to say to those friends waiting on Galveston Island? The groom left waiting at the wharf! What a laugh they'd have!

His friends didn't laugh. When they got him alone they began to plead.

"Thank heaven she didn't come!"

"Sam, you're no more suited to be a happy married man than—"

"Thanks for your warm wishes!"

"We're saying this for your own good!"

"It wouldn't last six months!"

"We can't lose you, Sam! You're too important to Texas! And if—if—"

"If this marriage failed and I went to pieces again? Is that what you're trying to say?"

"You say this girl is only—"

"Don't call her 'this girl'!" Sam roared with an oath. "Her name is Margaret Lea! And it's going to be Mrs. Sam Houston!"

"The daughter of a Baptist minister will certainly enjoy your language."

Sam started to roar again, stopped, and finally smiled. "You know, I suspect there are going to be some changes in one Sam Houston."

"Bah! Any girl who marries a man to reform him is—"

"She's not marrying me to reform me, you—" He stopped again.

His friends raised eyebrows, looked at one another, and walked away. After that no one tried to talk to Sam "for his own good," but he knew they were still talking.

In May of 1840 he and Margaret were married in her brother's stately home in Alabama. Sam thought again of the rugged frontier world that was Texas. Was he asking too much of Margaret?

"We'll stop in Nacogdoches on our way to San Augustine," he told Margaret. "I still have a friend or two there, but . . ."

He told her of the battles over the Cherokee lands.

Nacogdoches flocked to see Margaret. Polite—just very polite—at first. But in half an hour someone said, "Hey, we ought to have a barbecue!"

"You won this round!" Sam whispered.

Word had gone ahead about when they'd reach San Augustine. The whole countryside had gathered at a barbecue to greet them. Sam listened and beamed as people talked to Margaret.

"We've been hearing about you! But they didn't say half enough!"

"No, sir! You're prettier than *that!*"

Sam overheard other remarks—and wondered if Margaret heard them, too.

"He *does* look happy."

"Maybe it'll work out all right."

"Lord, I wish I could think it would!"

"I heard he drank cold water at that barbecue in Nacogdoches."

Margaret had heard. That night she said, "So people are worried about your marrying me?"

It wasn't any use to lie. "Yes, dear."

"Funny, isn't it? People will always believe that a woman can wreck something. Why won't they believe that a woman can help build something? Why—"

She stopped. Sam was emptying a saddlebag and had dumped out a handful of Indian heads.

"Oh, Sam! How delightful! Where did you get them?"

"I made them." He told her of his whittling during the session of Congress. "I started whittling them just to bedevil some of the representatives. But, you know, it helped me think things out. Does that sound crazy?"

"No, Sam. If you could sit in Congress and knit a—"

"What!"

"That's what women do sometimes when they're figuring something out. Somehow I can't imagine you knitting a sock."

He chuckled, then suddenly stopped. That next session of Congress . . . He told Margaret about the long, hard trip to Austin and the danger of the isolated town. Austin even had a palisade around it to protect it from Indians. Nobody ventured out after dark—for fear he'd lose his scalp.

"I'm not afraid," Margaret said. "Bad roads and Indians aren't going to keep us that far apart."

Something else could. Margaret wakened one night shaking with chills, then burning with fever. Malaria! Sam had almost died of it once. He was frantic. When Margaret was well enough to travel, he put her on a ship and sent her back to Alabama to stay until she was completely over it.

He went to Austin alone, pulled out his clasp knife, and started whittling.

President Lamar was still doing things in the grand manner. Heaven only knew what the debt of Texas was by now. The "red backs"—paper money Lamar had issued—sometimes sank to ten cents on the dollar.

But Lamar had one more grand scheme. This would recoup the fortunes of Texas! He wanted Congress to vote funds to send an expedition to Santa Fé. Over two hundred soldiers, all mounted, wagonloads of equipment, an expedition that would be the pride of Texas!

A Lamar man explained the glorious plan. Some congressmen cheered. Sam had a few questions.

"Aren't we working desperately to get a peace treaty with Mexico? Then why plan an invasion of Mexico?"

"Santa Fé is east of the Rio Grande!" the Lamar man shouted. "Part of Texas!"

"Before Mexico signs that peace treaty? Recognizes our boundaries?" Sam asked.

"This is not an invasion! It is a peaceful trading expedition!"

"A trading expedition?" Sam asked. "With over two hundred soldiers?"

Before the debate ended Sam had whittled one wagon, two oxen, and twenty muskets.

Congress turned down the glorious plan. They refused to vote money for the expedition.

Sam folded his clasp knife, dusted off shavings, and went to join Margaret. He took her to the little summer home he was building for them at Cedar Point, on Galveston Bay.

"It's not much," he said.

"But it's ours!" And Margaret's eyes glowed.

Sam whistled as he made shelves. He set up a forge and hammered out hooks and brackets. He must tell Margaret someday about the poor stuttering recruit who thought he was a blacksmith and ordered him to fix a musket. He'd tell Margaret how he had said, "I *am* a blacksmith! I'm a damn . . ." Hmmm. . . . "I *am* a blacksmith! I'm a *mighty good* blacksmith!" That's how he'd say it. He grinned. Yes, there had been some changes in Sam Houston!

Margaret never said anything about his swearing. When he exploded he always said, "Sorry, dear! I didn't mean to—"

"I know you didn't" was all she ever said.

At Cedar Point he showed her the lone wagon, two oxen, and twenty muskets. "At least we stopped that scheme," he said. "It was Lamar's craziest. Thank heaven his term ends in December. He can't succeed himself."

"Who will be the next president?" she asked.

Sam didn't know. Burnet, probably.

That night three men came to talk with Sam. They

chatted with Margaret. They admired Sam's blacksmith work. Then they asked Sam to "show them around the place."

When they had gone, Margaret smiled. "They asked you to run for president, didn't they?"

Yes, he admitted. No, he hadn't said he'd run. This needed some thinking about. The next three years would be much worse than Sam's first term. Heaven only knew what the debt would be by December.

"If you don't tackle the job, who will?" Margaret asked. "I mean—who will try to save Texas?"

"You want me to run?"

Margaret took her time about answering. "No, Sam, I really don't. I'd like for us just to build a life of our own and have time to be happy. But I know you will run."

"Why?"

"Because 'you'll never turn your back to save your life.' "

Sam pretended to groan. "Why did I ever tell you that?"

"Because it was important."

"Bless you." After a while he sighed and said, "It'll be a dirty campaign, Margaret. I'll be running against Burnet. You'll hear me accused of everything—including cowardice in the Texas Revolution."

"What!"

"Burnet wanted to have me court-martialed for not winning the war at the Colorado River."

Margaret's eyes flashed. "Why, that—that— It's a good thing my mother brought me up to be a lady!"

Sam hugged her, laughed, and was sober again. "The next three years will be grim. If we hadn't stopped that Santa Fé expedition, these next three years would be impossible."

A week later the news was all over Texas. Lamar had gone ahead with his plans for the expedition. Congress would not vote the money? Bah! That for Congress! Lamar had a half million printed in New Orleans and went ahead.

"When will it start?" Margaret asked.

"By the first of May at the latest," Sam said. The route led over the high plateau. The summer sun would burn off all the grass. There would be no feed for their animals.

In May the expedition was assembling. Over two hundred soldiers in their fine new uniforms. A handsome cannon with Lamar's name engraved on the barrel. Ten merchants with ten wagons of goods to trade.

Quite a few little hitches developed to delay them. Weeks passed. It was after the middle of June when they started.

"Maybe they'll realize it's too late and turn back," Sam said. "It's their only chance. If they don't—if they go on—well, if I had any sense I'd drop out of this race for president."

"But you won't," she said.

He brushed her chin with his fist. "Don't remind me of 'never turn your back'!"

"I don't have to remind you. You can't ever forget it." Then she asked, "What are the first things you'll try to do, Sam?"

"Get that peace treaty with Mexico! Confound it, it should have been signed back in thirty-six! *Before* Santa Anna was released! But Burnet bargained to send him home to Mexico before the secret treaty was signed. And I had to honor that bargain. We're still waiting for Santa Anna to live up to his end of it. Now—with this Santa Fé expedition—heaven knows what will happen between Mexico and Texas."

"After that?" Margaret asked.

"The other big thing is annexation to the United States. Right now I don't know which is more impossible!"

The campaign for president was as violent as Sam had said it would be. Texans listened to all the charges leveled against Sam, and voted him into office more than two to one over Burnet.

Sam and Margaret were living in Houston City by then. The Allen brothers had offered them the home that was built for the "Presidential Palace." It was in better shape than when Sam had lived in it. Soon Margaret made a real home of it. She had her piano, her harp, and some furniture from Alabama.

In December Mrs. Lea was coming for a visit. Sam left Margaret with friends in Houston City and went to Austin alone.

He appeared for his inauguration in a linsey-woolsey checked hunting shirt, worn pantaloons, and a broad-brimmed fur hat.

Texas had nothing, he told the crowd, but the courage and industry of her people. He was going to cut his salary in half. (Cheers.) He was going to cut some other salaries. (Pause, then cheers.)

Congress approved his economy drive. They were so enthusiastic—those congressmen—that they did not even vote the funds he needed to take care of day-by-day expenses.

Sam was writing another message to Congress about the fact that the government must have *some* money—when word of the Santa Fé expedition reached Texas.

The whole expedition had been captured! They were being treated like invaders! Being marched to Mexico City under brutal guards!

Congress shouted for war! Texas must invade Mexico. Sam tried to reason with them. Did they want to save the prisoners? Declare war, and every man would die.

He sent letters to Mexico City to the ministers from the United States and England, asking them to petition for the release of the prisoners.

Congress passed a bill demanding war. Sam vetoed it. Congress passed the bill over his veto—but failed to vote any funds to carry on the war. Sam let them adjourn.

Linsey-Woolsey President

He rode home to Margaret. No fiery steed and handsome trappings now. That would not go with his checked hunting shirt. He bought a mule. Besides, mules were better travelers on these roads.

Men jeered at the mule with his longish red-brown hair. Looked like a cinnamon bear!

Sam agreed. "I named him Bruin."

He set out on the five-day journey from Austin to Houston City. Bruin was a good traveler. He made it in two hours less than four days. Margaret was so delighted that she hugged Bruin.

She helped Sam unpack, found his latest carvings, and gasped. "Sam! They're skulls!"

"I was thinking of the Santa Fé expedition. Men died between Austin and Santa Fé. Men are dying on the march to Mexico City. And they'll all die—unless I can calm this war fever."

War fever was running high in Houston City and Galveston. Committees were raising money, raising armies, and appointing more committees to call on the president and see what he was going to do! Didn't Congress declare war? Yes, Sam agreed, but Congress failed to vote any money to carry on a war.

The shouting died down to a mutter.

Then a Mexican army raided San Antonio and nearby towns and carried off a hundred prisoners.

War cries rose to a scream. What was the president going to do? Sam wrote again to the ministers in Mexico City and asked for their help. He ordered out two companies of militia to guard the southwest coast. He directed Galveston to stand ready to repel an attack from the sea. But he flatly refused to order an invasion of Mexico.

Texans stormed. They demanded that he call a special session of Congress. He did. He called it to meet in Houston City. West Texas was up in arms. True— people had been leaving that isolated outpost ever since the raid on San Antonio. But how did their president dare to move the capital!

The special session of Congress met in June in Houston City. Sam requested that they settle the matter of a safe place for the capital. They did not.

Congress was too busy voting for war. They gave the president power to conscript one third of all able-bodied men in Texas. Money to wage the war? They took care of that handsomely. They gave the President permission to sell ten million acres of public land.

"Sell it how?" Sam growled. "How have it surveyed? How hire agents? They might as well give me permission to sell ten million acres of blue sky!" He put the bill on his desk—and left it there.

Rumors spread. He was going to veto the war bill! Threats spread even faster. If he vetoed that bill, he'd be assassinated!

Friends came around to plead with Sam. He had nothing to say. They begged Margaret to talk to him. She said it was up to Sam. They suggested a guard around his home. He only laughed. Friends stopped coming around, especially at night. If that fool man vetoed the bill—well, who wanted to get in the way of a bullet?

"You've made up your mind, haven't you, Sam?" Margaret said.

"How do you know?"

"You're not in a whittling mood."

"Right, dear. I've made up my mind."

He vetoed the bill.

Newspapers screamed for him to be impeached. Mass meetings met and said he should be impeached. One town burned him in effigy. Then the war fever died down.

West Texas was still fuming, though, over his moving the capital. Sam knew that people would never believe he moved it for any reason but because Houston City was named for him. In an effort to calm that storm he moved the capital to Washington-on-the-Brazos. Just at that moment Sam wondered—but never out loud—how long Texas would need a capital.

The national debt was staggering. The income would not even pay the interest on it. And Texas was on the brink of a war that would plunge her even deeper in debt.

Peace with Mexico . . . annexation to the United States. Both seemed hopeless.

Sam began whittling. What could make the North stop fighting the annexation of Texas? The threat of friendship between Texas and another power—England or France? What could ever settle the peace with Mexico? The threat to Mexico of trouble with a stronger power—England or France? Maybe . . . just maybe . . . those two problems could be solved together.

Dr. Ashbel Smith was taking care of Texan affairs in London and Paris. Sam could not write what was on his mind. He could not trust that information in the mails. And he couldn't afford a special messenger to carry letters between him and Dr. Smith. He would just have to depend on that canny gentleman to understand.

Dr. Smith had done an excellent job with Felix-the-Great. That time, though, Sam could explain his "Indian cunning." This time he could not. He would just have to hope.

"In a Whittling Mood"

Peace and annexation. During the stormy days of 1842 those goals looked farther away than ever. Texas seemed helpless and alone, ringed around with enemies. Even Nature joined the battle to conquer her. Insects destroyed over half the crops that summer. A hurricane battered Galveston and left a rubble of wrecked ships and tumbled walls.

If Sam ever gave up hope, nobody knew it. "Texas cannot be conquered!" he said. "Texas will plant again! Texas will build again! Texas will have peace and prosperity!"

Sometimes Margaret's eyes were full of shadows. But she never said, "What's the use?"

Sam never said it either. He even smiled sometimes— when he thought about it.

In May of 1843 he was smiling without even trying to. He was beaming. He and Margaret had a little son.

Mrs. Lea came to be with Margaret. She talked quite a bit to the baby. "Little Sam, your father is the most *idiotically* happy man I've ever seen. If your mother and

I don't watch out, he'll spoil you hopelessly!" But she smiled when she said it.

"Someday," Margaret said, "he'll be 'big-brothering' a little brother."

"Margaret!" Sam asked, "Don't you ever forget anything?"

"Not anything important."

Sam kissed her and went back to his office. The light often burned until two o'clock in the morning. It took a long time to carve out those letters he was sending—to Santa Anna, to the English minister in Mexico City, to Washington, D.C., to Ashbel Smith in far-off London.

Would Ashbel Smith understand the desperate game he was playing? Even if Smith does understand, Sam thought, he can't tell me that he does.

A two-month-old letter arrived from Ashbel Smith:

> . . . Oh, by the way! I met a chap the other day who reminded me of Felix-the-Great. Remember him? Remember the talks I had with him? . . .

That was all on that subject. But Sam heaved a sigh of relief. Yes, Ashbel Smith understood the game he was playing—pitting England and France against the United States.

Sam's letters to Mexico City began to take effect. Santa Anna finally released the prisoners of the Santa Fé expedition. He made quite a speech when he did release them:

"In a Whittling Mood"

Texans! The generous Mexican nation, whom you have offended, in recompense for her many favors, pardons you! And in the name of the Mexican people—always great—I restore you to that liberty which you lost by invading our territory and violating our domestic firesides! Return to your country and publish to her people that the Mexicans are as generous to the conquered as they are valiant on the field of battle! You have proved our valor! Now prove our magnanimity!

Sam gave all the credit to England. That great nation had helped the cause of humanity! That great nation . . .

Presently newspapers in the United States were spreading alarms. England was getting friendly with Texas! England had helped Texas deal with Mexico! If England got a foothold in Texas . . .

By the summer of 1844 James K. Polk was running for President of the United States with a slogan that favored annexation of Texas.

Texans were wild with enthusiasm. Men who had called for Sam's impeachment were shouting, "Hurrah for Houston!"

Sam's term as president would end in December of 1844. Texans elected his secretary of state, Anson Jones, to be their next president. Not because they thought much of Dr. Jones—but because he was "Houston's man." He'd do whatever Houston told him to do. President Houston could not succeed himself, but he could keep a hand on things.

Sam hoped he could. Anson Jones had developed ideas of grandeur, too. Anson Jones did not favor annexation. He saw a glorious future for Texas, the Lone Star Republic!

Polk won the election. Texans rang bells and lit bonfires to celebrate. Annexation was coming! It was only a matter of time!

In the United States, President Tyler, about to go out of office, evidently decided that he might as well get the credit for annexing Texas. He let it be known that if Texas would ask again for annexation . . .

Sam baffled the United States and angered Texans by saying "No!" Texas *had* asked to be annexed. She had been refused. She would not ask again. That was final!

While the United States simmered and Texas boiled, Sam went on talking to one Captain Elliot of England.

In December Sam's term ended. The matter of annexation was still hanging fire. "I'm at the peak of my unpopularity," he told Margaret. "Right now, I couldn't be elected collector of customs for a small port—a very small port."

Margaret smiled. "I guess maybe I'm glad. I think I've had enough of politics!"

They went north of Houston City to the plantation Sam had, a few miles from the little town of Huntsville. He called it Raven Hill. Woodland and pasture. Bird songs and flowers. Horses to ride. Before little Sam was two he would sit bareback on a gentle mare, hang on to her mane, and laugh.

"In a Whittling Mood"

News from the United States drifted in. President Tyler was still trying. Texas would not ask for annexation. The United States Senate would not vote for a treaty. Tyler could not get a two-thirds vote in the Senate. But a joint resolution offering annexation—that would take only a simple majority in the House and in the Senate. Just before President Tyler left office, Congress passed the resolution and he signed it.

One day a visitor rode up to Raven Hill—Jack Donelson, Old Hickory's nephew. He talked with Margaret. He agreed that little Sam was amazing for his age. Then he asked Sam to "show him around the plantation."

Jack Donelson was puzzled. He had come with an offer of annexation. President Jones had been cool. Surely Sam Houston could talk to him?

"I'm out of it," Sam said. "I've no power to—"

Jack Donelson said, "Bah!" He gave Sam the paper to read.

Sam read. Hmmmm. No wonder President Jones had been cool. Wasn't the United States taking a lot for granted? Laying down all those conditions about annexing Texas? The United States was not dealing with a piece of her own territory. She was dealing with the sovereign Republic of Texas!

Jack Donelson must have sent word home that "Old Hickory's boy" was being difficult. Andrew Jackson, old and sick, wrote to Sam, pleading with him to use his influence in favor of annexation.

"I'd rather take a beating than hurt him," Sam told

Margaret, "but I can't say anything now."

"What will Anson Jones do?" she asked.

"He'll accept annexation. He'll have to! The people of Texas will force him to! Maybe he'll feel better about it when he gets credit for bringing it off."

"And you?"

"We're going to have a vacation! We'll be on the next ship that sails from Galveston!"

On shipboard, Margaret squeezed Sam's hand. "You look ten years younger already. Oh, Sam, I'm so glad all the fighting is over! All the standing alone! You've been hissed and booed and blamed enough for one man!"

Sam laughed and gave one big stretch. It had been a long fight, but worth it. Mexico, through the English minister, had just offered a peace treaty—on the condition that Texas would never join the United States. Texans were really up in arms!

President Jones would call a special session of Congress to vote on annexation. Then the people would vote on it. That would be that!

His work was done! Now for a vacation! New Orleans first, for a week or two, then to see Old Hickory . . .

In New Orleans they heard that Old Hickory was very ill—was sinking. They took the first steamer north. Sam paced the deck, as though to will the boat to go faster. The engines broke down and delayed them twenty-four hours. In Nashville Sam ordered a coach and the fastest horses in Tennessee. They dashed toward The Hermitage.

Jack Donelson's wife met them at the door. Sam knew before she spoke that it was too late.

"Not an hour ago," she said.

In the room with Old Hickory's body Sam knelt and bowed his head against the old man's heart. If only he could have been in time! He and Old Hickory could have talked about how Sam fought for annexation by pretending to be against it.

Old Hickory would have laughed. He loved a good fight. And what a fighter he had been! Sam thought of the States' Rights dinner in 1830. Old Hickory had listened to all the toasts, hammering home Calhoun's stand on states' rights. Then Old Hickory had stood, had given his toast, and had waited until every man stood to drink it with him. "Our Union! It must be preserved!"

Texas would be part of that Union now. Kneeling beside his old chief, Sam made a vow: "Our Union! It must be preserved!"

In October Sam left Margaret and little Sam for a visit in Alabama and went home alone. He'd better be taking care of business, he said. Being president of Texas had not been a profitable occupation.

From Texas he wrote to Margaret. "The people voted for annexation a thousand to one. I am still at the peak of my unpopularity. They have not forgiven me for my 'obstruction' to annexation. Enjoy yourself, dear, and don't worry about the future. Texas will never interrupt our home life by electing me to office again."

February 16, 1846, the Lone Star Republic became the Lone Star State. Two days later the Senate of the new State of Texas elected senators to the United States Senate. One was Tom Rusk. The other was Sam Houston.

Sam found Margaret studying a map, tracing the long journey—over two thousand miles—from Texas to Washington.

"How long does a senator serve?" she asked.

"Six years. Of course, one of us won't serve that long. The two senators from a state aren't supposed to begin and end their terms at the same time. Tom and I will draw straws—something of the sort—and one will serve the full six years. The other will serve a shorter term." He smiled. "And you needn't say what you're hoping."

"All right, I won't." Presently Margaret said, "Well, at least you won't have to be in any brawls!"

Sam's first Sunday in Washington he wrote to Margaret. "Tom Rusk and I drew straws. Tom got the six-year term. I got a one-year term, until March, 1847."

His second Sunday he wrote, "I went to the E Street Baptist Church this morning. I told Dr. Samson that I came because of you—the best Christian I had ever known."

The next Sunday he wrote, "Dr. Samson admired the little heart I whittled this morning. I gave it to him."

"In a Whittling Mood"

Margaret would understand why he was in a whittling mood in church. He did not tell her that he was in a whittling mood in the Senate too. Margaret had hoped he wouldn't be in any more "brawls."

Less than two weeks in the Senate, and he had landed with both feet in a brawl. He was taking the unpopular side of the question.

"Traitor!"

President Polk had two questions to settle—the Oregon Territory boundary with England and the annexation of Texas with Mexico.

President Polk was not popular with his Senate. Whatever he suggested stirred up violent debates.

That Oregon boundary—would it be at the forty-ninth parallel? Some people were shouting "Fifty-four Forty or Fight!" President Polk recommended that the United States cancel the present treaty and start talking over things with England. The Senate exploded. The President was driving the country straight into war with England!

Sam—only two weeks in the Senate—got up to speak. The President's stand would not lead to war, not if the Senate stood back of him. But—if England saw division and dissension in the United States, then she might threaten war, thinking a divided country would back down.

Outside the Senate Sam talked long and hard. The United States must not have division and dissension.

"Traitor!"

Look at the Mexican situation. Mexico threatened to go to war against the United States over the annexation of Texas. Mexico—who had lost a war with the little Republic of Texas. Why would she threaten war against the United States? Only because she had seen ten years of division and dissension over the annexation of Texas. She would threaten war because she believed that a country divided would back down.

Sam's fellow Senators listened and rubbed their chins. Did Senator Houston think war was coming with Mexico?

War with Mexico, Sam declared, isn't *coming*. It has been *going on* since 1835. Yes, that war would continue. And when it was over the United States would own everything from Louisiana to the Pacific Ocean. California—and all the land between California and Texas. Mexico had proved that she couldn't settle the territory or rule the territory. Mexico could not even establish just rule south of the Rio Grande!

The Mexican War began in April. President Polk offered Sam a command. Sam refused. He had fought his share of the war with Mexico.

He went home for the summer. It was important to be home. In September a little daughter was born. Mrs. Nancy Lea was with Margaret.

They named the baby Nancy Elizabeth after her two grandmothers. They called her Nannie. Sometimes Sam forgot and called her Nannie Lea.

Mrs. Lea talked to the baby. "Your father," she would say, "is a politician! Once a politician, always a politician. Besides he's full of Indian cunning!"

"Maybe not a politician," Sam told her. "My term in the Senate ends next March."

In January of 1847 Texans voted for Sam to return for a term of six years, until 1853. The Mexican War was going on. Perhaps men were remembering San Jacinto.

That summer Sam built a home in Huntsville. If he had to be gone much of the time for the next six years, Raven Hill was too far out in the country.

Early in 1848 the Mexican War ended. Sam's predictions about territory came true. And the Oregon question had been settled. Now the United States stretched from coast to coast.

When Sam got home that summer Texans met him with smiles. General Taylor and General Scott hadn't won all that territory, they said. The most important battle against Mexico had been fought—and won—at San Jacinto. They cheered Sam again. It took a long time to say "Sam Houston, the hero of San Jacinto." They shortened it to "Sam Jacinto!"

Sam shook hands, waved, and hurried home to Huntsville. He had a new little daughter to meet—named Margaret Lea and called Maggie.

Margaret was beaming. "Oh, Sam, it's so good to be alive!" Then, to his bewilderment, her voice shook. "To hear you being *praised!* I—I don't think I could go through some of those years again. I—" She bit her lips and managed to smile. "You know, you're awfully far away in Washington, but at least—back here in Texas now—I'm among *friends* when you're gone." And she began to sob. "It was so awful, Sam! When you were standing alone all the time!"

"Margaret! I never knew you felt that way!"

"How would *you* have felt if people had been c-c-cursing *me* all the time?"

"One word about you, and I'd have cut someone's heart out!"

"But women can't go around cutting out hearts. We just have to hear it." Presently she smiled. "Silly!" she said. "I'll not do that again."

The spring of 1850 Sam was waiting for each letter from home. Margaret was saying, "I hope we'll have a little brother for Sam to start bringing up."

Sam wrote back, "If he's a boy, we'll name him Andrew Jackson Houston."

When word finally came from Margaret, she wrote, "You must help think of a name for her. She's a solemn-looking little darling—but bright. Not just because they're our children, Sam, but don't you think . . ."

That summer Sam spent a lot of time in the little log building in their yard that he called his office. The children hung around, watching him whittle. Four-year-old

Nannie was very "big-sisterly" toward little Maggie, and very proud of Mary, the new baby.

Margaret smiled with the children over the toys, but when she was alone with Sam her eyes were troubled. Finally she asked, "What is it, dear?"

"What is what?"

"What's put you in a whittling mood?"

For the first time he lied to her. "Nothing, dear. Seems I've just got the habit. And the children do like the toys."

"I see." Margaret smiled and left him.

Sam began to whittle a top to spin—and thought about the trouble that was brewing. The rift between North and South was growing wider. Back in 1820 Henry Clay had healed the breach with the Missouri Compromise. Could anyone heal it again?

Back in Washington that winter Sam found that Henry Clay was going to try to heal the breach again. He was going to ask both North and South to give a little—for the sake of peace.

Sam read the terms of the Compromise of 1850. Any senator, he thought, who voted for that compromise, was going to be crucified by the extremists in his own section—the violent abolitionists in the North or the violent "states' righters" in the South.

As the debate went on, Sam left many a pile of shavings under his seat in the Senate. At last he wrote to Margaret. "I'm sorry, dear, but you're going to hear me 'cursed' again. I'll be called 'a traitor to the South.' But it isn't a vote for North or South. It's a vote to save the Union!"

He voted for the Compromise of 1850.

No cheering crowds delayed his trip to Huntsville that summer.

Margaret only said, "Sometimes, Sam, when you were president, things boiled up and then—sort of—simmered down."

"We can hope!"

Things did "simmer down" a bit. At least, in 1853, Texas returned Sam to the Senate for another six years, until 1859.

"I'm so glad things are finally peaceful!" Margaret said.

Sam kissed the top of her head. He would not tell her what he feared—that he could feel the rumblings underneath the calm. He thought of the vow he had made by Old Hickory's body. "Our Union! It must be preserved!" He'd live up to that. He'd fight to save the Union—even though someday he might be hissed and booed as never before.

But he would not talk of it now. Margaret might have long enough for tears. Let this summer be happy. And it was such a happy home. Young Sam had four little sisters now. Both Sam and Margaret admitted they had prayed for a son. But Nellie was a darling baby.

That summer Sam made toys for the girls. Young Sam said he was too big for toys. He was ten. Sam nodded. He remembered being ten. He and young Sam had long talks together. They spoke of the girls as "the children."

At last the day came when Sam was packing for Washington.

"I think this has been the happiest summer we've ever had!" Margaret said.

He smiled and agreed. He kept the smile on through all the good-bys. Then the dark cloud settled over him. What was it that he felt coming?

Texas . . . his Texas. She had never looked so beautiful. What was it that haunted him? What trouble was brewing? When was it coming, and how? Slowly, day by day? Or very suddenly?

Trouble came, as the saying was, "like a bolt from the blue." Senator Douglas presented the Kansas-Nebraska Bill to the Senate with a section that threatened to rip the Union apart. That section wiped out the Missouri Compromise. It provided that settlers in that territory should make their own choice about whether their land would be slave or free.

Why had Senator Douglas done it? Some men said because he was courting favor with the South to get enough votes to be elected President.

Whatever the reason, the bill stirred up a storm more savage than any North-South argument before.

The rumor spread that Sam Houston—a southerner and a Democrat—was going to speak against the bill! A correspondent of the Richmond *Enquirer* wrote:

"Traitor!"

I hear that General Sam Houston will vote against the Kansas-Nebraska Bill. . . .

Nothing can justify this treachery; nor can anything save the traitor from the deep damnation which such treason may merit.

Sam's friends begged him not to speak against the bill. It already had enough votes to pass. It was useless to speak against it. Why ruin himself for a lost cause?

Sam did not answer. He wrote to Margaret. "I cannot turn my back!"

He spoke against the bill. He pleaded with the South to uphold the Compromise. "If you tear it and scatter it to the wind, you will reap the whirlwind!"

Sam had never stirred up such a storm as raged around him now. The Texan Congress passed a resolution that Sam Houston would not be returned to Congress for another term. Newspapers said that if he had a shred of decency he'd resign now. Papers throughout the South branded him a traitor.

There was only one bright spot in Sam's world that summer. Little Andrew Jackson Houston was born. Sam, Margaret, and the older little sisters accused one another of spoiling him. Young Sam was too big for that sort of thing. He was eleven.

He came to Sam's office one day with a newspaper, and asked, "Why don't you resign? If Texas doesn't want you, *we* do!"

"Thanks!" Sam smiled. "Anyhow, I'll not be going

back after fifty-nine. Texas has promised me that! Then we'll have lots of time."

Young Sam didn't smile. "I'll be sixteen then."

"Sixteen! Good Lord! How time flies!"

"Not here at home," young Sam muttered. "Just women and girls. Now a baby. Why *don't* you resign?"

"I never told you about when I marched off to war the first time, did I? You see . . ." When he had finished, Sam asked, "Now, you understand?"

"No, sir. That was *fighting*. This is just talking."

"Why, you little . . ." Sam exploded, then apologized. "I'm sorry, son. Forgive me. When I was your age, I couldn't have understood, either."

"You never talked to me about fighting before."

"Didn't I? I only fought in one battle in the War of Eighteen-twelve. But in the Texas Revolution . . ."

They talked till the shadows grew long.

Young Sam's eyes were shining. "I hope there's a war I can go to!"

Sam almost exploded again. He must not do that. He had whittled long and prayerfully over one question. Now he had made up his mind.

That November Sam was baptized. He joined the church.

Margaret's eyes were bright with tears. "Oh, Sam, I wish you were done with Washington. We could be so happy—just all of us together."

"Our eldest son agrees." And Sam told her of young Sam's views on real fighting compared to "just talking."

"Traitor!"

Margaret gasped. "Why that little . . ." She stopped. "Poor blessed. I guess he's been reading the papers. I've found it hard enough to face what people have said of you. Why should I expect a little boy to understand? How can I help him, Sam?"

"I don't know, Margaret. Maybe—let him feel he's the man of the house when I'm gone."

"He already lords it over the girls."

"I suppose so. But maybe we can just let him lord it a bit?"

"Sam, dear, you're a wonderful father!"

"No, I'm not. I haven't had time to be." He thought again of young Sam's face when he said, "I'll be sixteen then."

"You take time when you're home."

"I guess that isn't enough," Sam said.

When he started back to Washington he took young Sam with him as far as Galveston. "They say when the railroads get through, it'll only take eight days from Washington to Texas. That'll be fine, won't it?"

"Yes, sir," young Sam said obediently.

Sam thought of his answers to grown-ups when he knew it was better to be polite.

In Galveston he said, "Good-by, son. Take care of the women and children for me, will you?"

"Yes, sir!" Young Sam saluted.

Sam could have hugged him. He just returned the salute. He could remember when he was Sam's age.

Only, he thought, he had been able to be proud of his father. He had never had to know he was called a traitor. Maybe—just maybe—the rest of his time in Washington he wouldn't have to stir up the newspapers again.

The next time Sam decided he'd have to stir up the newspapers was the summer of 1857 when he was home, in Texas.

He talked it over with Margaret first. Then he said, "I think we'd better have a 'council of war.' Sam, Nannie, and Maggie. They can all read. I'd better make them understand. At least I'd better try to!"

"You'll Never
Turn Your Back"

Yes, the three oldest children had better know what was coming. Young Sam was fourteen, Nannie was eleven, and Maggie was nine. Very bright children. They read just fine! And there was going to be plenty to read!

That night, after the younger children were asleep, Sam and Margaret held their "council of war" with the three older ones.

"I'm going to run for governor of Texas," Sam told them. "And I'm not going to win. Sounds funny, doesn't it? To run when I know I won't win? But I'm going to run because it'll give me a chance to make a lot of speeches. And I've got a lot of things I want to say! Now, it's going to be a pretty rough campaign. You'll read a lot of things about me in the papers. And I'm not going to win. You understand?"

The children stared at him, big-eyed and solemn. They promised to "understand."

But when Sam lost the election, Nannie and Maggie wept. He had come so close! Over 28,000 votes! The other man got fewer than 33,000!

"I did what I set out to do," Sam told them. "I started a lot of people thinking." He grinned at young Sam. "Twenty-eight thousand people are thinking mighty straight."

Young Sam muttered about something he had to do and left the room.

Sam couldn't blame him. It *had* been a rough campaign. It had been so savage that one editor—though he was against Sam—had finally said it wasn't sporting "to kick a dead lion." What boy wanted to hear his father called "a dead lion"? How, Sam thought, could he expect the boy to bear up under that? How, he added, could he have asked it of Margaret?

That winter in Washington a senator taunted Sam from the floor of the Senate. How did it feel to be twice rejected by his home state? First, a resolution passed that he would not be re-elected in 1859—now defeated for governor of his state.

Sam was smiling when he got up to answer the taunt. Before he was done speaking, most of the Senators were laughing with him. But back home, Sam knew, a certain boy was not laughing. He was remembering that his father was called "a dead lion."

The spring of 1859 Sam was serving his last term in the Senate. Just before the close of the session he made a farewell speech. Word must have gotten around. When Sam entered the Senate that day the galleries were jammed and people were standing.

Sam closed his speech with a prayer that Congress would have the wisdom to keep the peace and to save the Union.

He went home to Texas. How good it was to be home!

Five-year-old Andrew had a little brother Willie now. Only, as Andrew said, Willie wasn't really a *brother* yet. He was just a *baby*.

Sam promised that Willie would get over being a baby. "You did, you know. You're quite a boy now!"

Young Sam was sixteen and lord of the household—very lordly! But, alone with Sam, he was very young and troubled. "You're really done with politics now?"

"I hope so!"

Young Sam heaved a big sigh. "Man, I'm *glad!*"

A week later Sam was whittling.

Margaret said nothing for two days. Then she asked, "Shall we call another 'council of war'?"

"You aren't very easy to fool, are you?" Sam said.

"I don't know, dear. You never tried to fool me but once. Back in fifty, I think it was."

Sam blinked, then grinned.

"We'd better have Mary, too, hadn't we, for this 'council of war'? She's nine now. She reads very well. Tonight?"

Sam nodded and dropped another shaving.

That night when the little ones were asleep the six of them sat together. The girls were solemn. Young Sam was tense.

"I promised myself when I came home that I was through with politics," Sam said. "But I find I can't be. I'm going to run for governor again. I've got to. Texas is drifting toward two things that must not be! Secession—breaking away from the Union—and reopening the African slave trade. No civilized nation in the world engages in the African slave trade now! If Texas did, she would be disgraced! I've got to stop it! You understand?" Then he added, "I probably won't have to do much campaigning. The newspapers will do my talking for me."

The newspapers did do his talking for him. The anti-Houston papers laughed at the idea of "the dead lion" running for governor. Didn't Houston know when he was through? Didn't he know he could never win another election in Texas? And certainly not on a Union platform! But the pro-Houston papers hammered on the disgrace of reopening the African slave trade. And . . . people had been thinking. Some of them had been thinking for two years, since the campaign of 1857. They elected Sam governor of Texas.

The girls all tried to hug Sam at the same time. Young Sam had an ear-to-ear grin that wouldn't wipe off.

The governor's family made quite an impression on

"You'll Never Turn Your Back"

Austin. Young Sam, six feet tall and very handsome in his new uniform, came home sometimes from the military academy in Bastrop. All the other children were home. The girls went to school in Austin and studied Latin and music with their mother. Four girls—but the home generally echoed with the laughter of a dozen.

"Does the noise ever bother you?" Margaret asked once.

"I love it!" Sam told her.

"The children love having you home. They're so happy, Sam."

But sometimes Margaret's eyes were very thoughtful. She knew Sam had run for governor for just one reason—to save the Union—to keep Texas from seceding.

The fall of 1860 the "Black Republicans" of the North elected Abraham Lincoln President of the United States. The Union began to fall apart. In the South one state after another seceded. Sam had not had to campaign much for governor. But now he campaigned endlessly against secession.

Once more he was standing alone.

In one place people refused to let him speak in the town hall.

"You have a right to refuse to let me speak in that hall," Sam agreed. "I did not help pay for it. But you cannot refuse to let me speak outside—on the soil of Texas! I did help pay for it! I helped pay for it with my blood!"

A yell went up. "Yeah, Sam Jacinto!"

But there began to be threats against his life.

In Galveston the owners of a hall refused to let him use it. Nothing personal, they said. But if he spoke in Galveston, he'd be assassinated. They just didn't want that to happen in their hall.

Sam said he would speak from the balcony of his room in Tremont House.

The owner of Tremont House shrugged. Whatever Governor Houston wanted. . . . But he disappeared suddenly.

In a few minutes some of Sam's friends came dashing in, breathing hard. Was it true that he was going to speak from his balcony? To crowds in the street below?

They pleaded with Sam. He must not run the risk! Galveston was in an ugly mood.

"I've charged enemy lines before," Sam said. He stepped out on the balcony and looked down on the crowd.

They hissed and booed. Sam waited. The noise grew louder. He still waited. Finally the noise began to die down.

Someone yelled, "Yeah, Sam Jacinto!"

A cheer ran through the crowd. Sam waited for silence. Then he talked to the people of the tragedy he saw in store if the Union was wrecked.

> . . . Some of you laugh to scorn the idea of bloodshed as a result of secession, and jocularly propose

to drink all the blood that will ever flow in consequence of it. But let me tell you what is coming on the heels of secession. The time will come when your fathers and husbands, your sons and brothers, will be herded together like sheep at the point of a bayonet, and your mothers and wives, and sisters and daughters, will ask, "Where are they?" and echo will answer "Where?"

A deep silence fell on the crowd. They were thinking now. If only enough people would listen—would think. . . .

But Texas seceded from the Union and joined the South. Texas demanded that all her officials take an oath of allegiance to the Confederacy.

For days Sam left a pile of shavings by his chair in his study. Three-year-old Willie hung around, beaming.

Andrew was going on seven and very big-brotherly. "Here, Willie! This is for you!"

And he explained to Willie about little Temple. He was just a *baby* now, but someday he'd be a *brother*.

"Won't he?" Andrew asked Sam. "Won't he get bigger and be a brother? Like Willie did?" Andrew wasn't getting any answers. He pounded Sam's knee. "You're not listening to me!"

Sam looked up blankly for a moment, then smiled and hugged both boys. "Later, son. You and Willie run along now."

He patted the seats of their pants. He watched them go out. He turned to his desk. He started to pick up his pen. Then he sat with his head in his hands.

He knew what he was going to say. He knew what the result was going to be. Texas was going to throw him out of the governor's chair. . . . What was that Latin phrase? *Morituri salutamos?* Was that it? Back in the days when Christians had been thrown into the arena to fight lions, that was what they said to the crowd. "We who are about to die salute you."

He was going to seal his doom when he refused to take the oath of allegiance to the South. He began to write:

> I love Texas too much to bring strife and blood-
> shed on her. . . .

Then, because he knew what was coming, he closed with these words:

> I am stricken down now because I will not yield
> those principles which I have fought for and
> struggled to maintain. The severest pang is that
> the blow comes in the name of the State of Texas.

Sam was late starting home one evening in March. He had been dawdling. He admitted it to himself. Dawdling —because he didn't want to tell Margaret what he'd have to tell her now. Somehow he had not thought of this. He should have.

"You'll Never Turn Your Back"

When he refused to take the oath, he knew he'd be thrown out of office. Why hadn't he stopped to think of the rest of it—that Margaret and the children would be thrown out of the Governor's Mansion?

So, as he admitted, he had dawdled. Just as he had done, almost fifty years ago, before he faced his mother and told her he had enlisted as a common soldier.

Mother had understood. But that, as young Sam would say, was about *fighting*. This was *just about words*. Would Margaret feel it had been a senseless stand to take?

He reached the door and stopped. He could hear the laughter of a dozen girls. Perhaps Margaret would be busy and he could go to his study and . . .

But Margaret opened the door for him, looked at his face, then stepped outside and closed the door behind her. "What is it, Sam?"

"We'll have to start packing. The one-time governor is about to be evicted."

Margaret bowed her head against his chest. Her hands gripped his arms.

He touched her cheek and felt tears. "I'm sorry, dear. Go on and cry. I've asked too much of you. A lot of times."

"You dear, dear idiot!" Her voice was shaky. "I'm not crying because I'm sad. Because I'm proud. I've been proud of you—so proud—so many times. But never as proud as I am now. Oh, Sam . . ."

Did Margaret say it, or was he hearing it out of the past, as he had heard it so many times . . . *You'll never turn your back.*

Margaret looked up. Her smile trembled but it was a smile. "Come in, Sam. The door is open to a brave man."

Format by Natalie Shalita
Set in Garamond
Composed, printed and bound by American Book–Stratford Press
HARPER & ROW, PUBLISHERS, INCORPORATED